SOLVING EMERGENCY DEPARTMENT OVERCROWDING

Successful Approaches to a Chronic Problem

Bud Pate

Derenda S. Pete, RN, MBA

Solving Emergency Department Overcrowding: Successful Approaches to a Chronic Problem is published by HCPro, Inc.

Copyright 2004 HCPro, Inc.

ISBN 1-57839-352-3

HCPro, Inc., provides information resources for the health care industry.

HCPro, Inc., is not affiliated in any way with the Joint Commission on Accreditation of Healthcare Organizations, which owns the JCAHO trademark.

The JCAHO continues to make changes to its new *Shared Visions—New Pathways*® survey process. As a result, certain terms referenced in this book may change after publication. To keep current with the JCAHO process, HCPro suggests reading *Briefings on JCAHO*, a monthly newsletter published by HCPro, and regularly checking our *accreditinfo.com* Web site.

Bud Pate, REHS, Co-author   Matthew Sharpe, Graphic Artist
Derenda S. Pete, RN, MBA, Co-author   D. René Molina, Layout Artist
Molly Hall, Managing Editor   Jean St. Pierre, Creative Director
Amy Anthony, Managing Editor   Tom Philbrook, Cover Designer
Matthew Cann, Group Publisher   Suzanne Perney, Publisher
Mike Mirabello, Senior Graphic Artist

Advice given is general. Readers should consult professional counsel for specific legal, ethical, or clinical questions.

Arrangements can be made for quantity discounts. For more information, contact:

HCPro, Inc.
P.O. Box 1168
Marblehead, MA 01945
Telephone: 800/650-6787 or 781/639-1872
Fax: 781/639-2982
E-mail: customerservice@hcpro.com

Visit HCPro at its World Wide Web sites:
www.hcpro.com, www.hcmarketplace.com, www.accreditinfo.com

Rev. 05/2004
19297

Contents

CONTENTS

About the Authors

Bud Pate, REHS

Bud Pate. REHS, joined The Greeley Company after 15 years at Kaiser Permanente where he was responsible for a wide range of quality and compliance initiatives during his tenure at Kaiser's Southern California Region, including standards and survey processes established by the Joint Commission on Accreditation of Healthcare Organizations (JCAHO), the Centers for Medicare & Medicaid Services, the California Department of Health Services (DHS), and the Office of Statewide Health Planning and Development. A nationally recognized expert in health care operations and compliance, he chaired the Joint Committee on Accreditation of the California Healthcare Association and regional health care councils for many years. He also represented the American Hospital Association on JCAHO's Standards Review Task Force, the Hospital Advisory Committee, and various other JCAHO work groups and panels. His publications include articles on root cause analysis and JCAHO survey processes. Pate is a prolific and engaging speaker on a variety of topics ranging from quality/performance improvement, diagnosing and treating blame, a "how to" of root cause analysis, surviving external surveys, the Emergency Medical Treatment and Active Labor Act, and other compliance and quality topics. He led Kaiser teams in the development of industry-leading processes for the integration of health plan and hospital credentialing, procedural/moderate sedation and best practice–driven assessments of emergency departments.

Pate's passion for departmental improvement was spawned in 2000 when Kaiser contracted with InSight Advantage to improve emergency department operations in Southern California. Through Kaiser's success, he was reacquainted with the power of data to drive improvement and the synergy between efficient departmental operations, high-quality patient care, and regulatory compliance.

Before coming to Kaiser Permanente in 1988, he was the supervisor of the Acute and Ancillary Services Section of the Los Angeles County DHS, Health Facilities Division. Prior to that Pate held a number of positions with the Los Angeles County DHS. He taught epidemiology at Washington Technical Institute in Washington, DC, and has lectured in many settings, including programs sponsored by the National Institute for Occupational Safety and Health, the Institute for Healthcare Improvement, the University of California at Los Angeles, California State University in Northridge, and the California Medical Association.

Pate received his Bachelor of Arts degree from the University of California at Los Angeles and a Certificate in Environmental Management from the University of Southern California School of Public Administration. He is a Registered Environmental Health Specialist in the state of California.

Derenda S. Pete, RN, MBA

Derenda S. Pete, RN, MBA, is a nationally recognized health care facilitator and emergency services clinician with experience as project director, senior consultant, health care administrator, and department manager. As a managing partner of InSight Advantage, she helps institutions across the country address difficult operational issues. By combining her knowledge of best demonstrated practices with profound data analysis skills and practical clinical/operational expertise, she has guided her clients toward improved customer service and profitability. Her approach, which typically focuses on labor optimization and process redesign, has been successful in maximizing her clients' functional capacity and improving their return on investment (ROI).

Pete is the co-creator of industry-leading departmental redesign software and review processes. She serves as faculty to Urgent Matters, an emergency department improvement effort organized by George Washington University and funded by a Robert Wood Johnson Foundation grant.

She was a paramedic and flight nurse associated with Herman Life Flight in Houston, TX. She received her Masters in Business Administration from Houston Baptist University and worked with institutions across the country on behalf of such consulting firms as West Hudson, Empath, and Adams and Associates.

Preface

Emergency departments: The anvil of health care

Anvil (noun): a solid object against which seemingly unbendable objects are hammered.

EMTALA sheds light on troubled ED operations

In 2000, one health care delivery system with 11 hospitals could not get its EMTALA[1] act together. Despite years of training and collaboration with emergency department (ED) managers and physicians, the system suffered a string of violations. These problems did not result from neglect nor ignorance. In fact, the system had extensive expertise about the details of EMTALA and had established a robust oversight process (including internal compliance reviews, oversight committees, etc.).

What, then was the cause of this string of EMTALA violations? The answer is simple: The system's EDs were operating beyond their functional capacity. Their current approach to care delivery provided neither the space nor the human resources to care for the onslaught of patients in their EDs. If an ED cannot keep pace with demand, it will have trouble meeting EMTALA expectations.

Ultimately, the system was able to fix its EMTALA problems, but not until it realized that the problem was not compliance readiness but the efficiency of its operations. By focusing on increasing efficiency, enhancing quality and safety, and decreasing cost, the system's EDs have gone two years and nearly two million patient visits without a single EMTALA hitch.

You might say "What? Fix a compliance issue AND improve operations? Unheard of! Compliance is a cost of doing business, overhead that must be suffered!" This book will demonstrate that quality and compliance are the natural byproduct of efficiency.

By working successfully with health care systems across the country, the authors validated their instinct that complying with the law is as simple (or as complex) as providing high-quality, efficient care. The best way—perhaps the only way—to achieve long-term, stable compliance is to focus on effective clinical operations. It also happens to be the best way to become and remain profitable.

[1] EMTALA: The federal Emergency Medical Treatment and Active Labor Act, sometimes referred to as COBRA.

Health care in crisis

The ED is a hospital's window to the community and should contribute at least 20% to its financial bottom line[2]. Yet EDs across the country are overcrowded, with long waits and frequent paramedic diversions that rob the institution and the community of vital resources. In fact, despite increasing volumes and patient acuities, fewer and fewer hospitals in California even offer emergency services, the number of licensed EDs in the state declined by 41 between 1990 and 2002.

In a recent nationwide survey, the United States General Accounting Office outlined the bounds of the problem[3]. Overall, approximately two-thirds of the nation's EDs were forced to divert paramedics at least part of the time. About 10% of all departments diverted paramedics 20% or more of the time. The problem is far worse in areas with large populations (more than 2.5 million inhabitants), areas with a high proportion of uninsured individuals, and areas experiencing significant growth over the last decade.

Why is diversion of paramedics such a widespread problem? The obvious answer is that many hospitals are operating beyond their functional capacity. Patients stay in telemetry beds and post-anesthesia recovery units for want of medical/surgical beds; patients stay in intensive care units for want of telemetry or step-down beds; patients are boarded in the ED for want of intensive care beds; and patients stay in paramedic ambulances for want of ED beds.

These clogged systems are one symptom of an industry-wide "melt down," which began as the aging population started to interfere with the tail of the Medicare funding bubble.

As baby boomers age, they tend to have more chronic illnesses. There are more of us with chronic obstructive pulmonary disease, more beset with congestive heart failure, and more who suffer from the long-term effects of diabetes. However, no one seems to be rushing to build more hospital beds to treat these illnesses. Instead, health care capital is invested in new radiology equipment and outpatient surgery centers, enterprises that promise an assured return on investment.

Although government leaders are quick to acknowledge the problem, there is little they can do short of redesigning the health care system from top to bottom. Solutions—at least in the short term—remain in the hands of hospitals. If a hospital is to survive while the larger societal issues are pondered, it must

---

[2] *California Health Care Foundation, California's Emergency Departments: System Capacity and Demand*
[3] *United States General Accounting Office, Hospital Emergency Departments: Crowded Conditions Vary among Hospitals and Communities, March 2003.*

successfully cope with the disconnect between the needs of the community and the ability of the hospital to absorb patients.

There are a number of articles, Web sites, and seminars that discuss sweeping cures to the problem (the "smoothing" of surgeries, designing departments based on queuing theory, etc.). Although these and other approaches are promising, we have chosen to instead focus on the details of how to cope and how to improve.

This book catalogues and explains effective approaches to this daunting problem, one subprocess, one data set, and one best practice at a time.

What is queuing theory?

Queuing theory is a mathematical model developed by John Nash and others to predict how many "servers" are necessary to accommodate an uneven flow.

Massachusetts has used queuing theory over the past few years to estimate the required capacity of hospital nurseries. Some hope queuing theory will also prove useful in designing ED systems.

The University of Alberta (Canada) has information and formulas available for those interested in pursuing this approach. We will discuss its possible use in the body of this book.

What is smoothing?

Litvak, Abbot, and Cooper (*Emergency Department Diversion: Causes and Solutions*, Academic Emergency Medicine, November 2001) believe the bane of hospital efficiency to be variability.

They describe three kinds of natural (unavoidable) variability:

- Clinical variability (variations in patient need)
- Flow variability (variations in patent volumes)
- Professional variability (variations in the skills of the practitioners available to care for the patients)

However, there is at least one variable that is (or should be) under the control of the institution: variation in the volume of elective surgeries. Litvac, et al, believe that smoothing the volume of elective surgeries will allow for more efficient use of operating rooms and hospital beds and ease ED crowding. We will discuss smoothing in more detail later in this book.

Increasing functional capacity rather than physical capacity

It would be wonderful if a hospital's physical capacity and staffing levels could expand like a sponge to absorb the unmet health care needs of the community it serves. Unfortunately, expanding a hospital's physical capacity is costly and time consuming. Hiring additional qualified staff becomes more difficult with each passing day.

Because it is easier to increase the capacity of the ED than of the inpatient tower, many institutions have increased the number of ED beds. While the number of licensed EDs in California decreased from 405 to 364 between 1990 and 2000 (a 10% reduction), the total number of ED beds increased by 19%.[4] This increase in ED beds, however, has made little impact on the overcrowding problem.

How then does a hospital cope with demands for service that exceed even long-term projections for increased physical capacity? They must increase "functional capacity" by maximizing efficiency. They must find ways to use the staff and the space they already have more efficiently. They must increase bed density[5] while ensuring quality, safe, satisfying patient care.

This book is designed to present practical, proven approaches to high-quality, efficient hospital care. It focuses on the seven "subprocesses" that describe the flow of ED patients:

Subprocess 0: Leadership . . . the context for change

Subprocess 1: ED intake (from registration and triage to examination by the emergency medicine physician)

Subprocess 2: ED throughput (diagnosing the patient's medical problem and providing stabilizing care and treatment)

Subprocess 3: ED output (patient discharge and transfer from the ED)

Subprocess 4: Inpatient intake (transferring patients to inpatient and long-term observation units)

Subprocess 5: Inpatient throughput (the patient's hospital stay, typically measured by his or her "length of stay")

Subprocess 6: Inpatient output (the discharge and transfer process from inpatient and long term observation units)

Hospitals across the country have been working to improve each of these subprocesses. Their efforts have yielded a wealth of benchmark data and "best demonstrated practices." This book catalogues that informa-

---

4 *California Health Care Foundation, Ibid.*
5 *"Bed density" is the number of patients seen per staffed emergency bed. It is the inverse of length of stay.*

tion and addresses approaches, such as Toyota's "Lean" improvement technique, that show promise for quick improvements. It also helps the institution establish quality "safety rails" to be certain that care is not compromised in the name of efficiency.

How to use this book as a reference

The tips and approaches discussed in this book often contain flags and comments, sort of like "ED Overcrowding for Dummies" [we love those books].

The **"Consider this When"** box is intended to give a context for the topic, indicating when and where these approaches work best.

The following logos are also used throughout the text:

Data—Means the topic is aimed at producing meaningful information to drive improvement and facilitate management.

Push—Means the topic is designed to "push" patients into the next subprocess.

Pull—Means the topic is designed to "pull" patients from the previous subprocess.

Flow—Means the topic aids the flow through the current subprocess.

Safe—Means that the issue is important for patient safety or regulatory/accreditation compliance.

Introduction

Getting to know the emergency care process
When health care sneezes, the ED gets pneumonia

What does an overcrowded emergency department (ED) look like?

- Patients spend more time in the waiting room than in a treatment bay
- A high percentage of patients leave before receiving a medical examination
- Physicians, nurses, and patients are dissatisfied
- Paramedic ambulances are diverted to other institutions

"[ED overcrowding] is a symptom of an entire health care system under extreme crisis," says Dr. Howard Koh, former commissioner of public health in Massachusetts.

So what causes overcrowding? Many factors:

- University hospitals have problems with patient lengths of stay. Residents, interns, and medical students participate extensively in patient care. Thus, the admitting history and physical takes more time, more repeat testing and consultation must occur to arrive at a treatment plan, and there is less certainty about discharge. The inpatient length of stay increases, and the ED becomes overcrowded.

- Private community hospitals depend on surgeries and other procedures for income. The more successful the hospital, the more time surgeons spend in the operating room. However, the more OR time, the fewer available beds for admissions from the ED, and the ED becomes overcrowded.

- For a number of reasons, elective surgery schedules are feast or famine. In a given day, surgery volumes swing from very low to very high. The high volume of patients leaving surgery typically occur at about the same time that the ED has a lot of patients requiring admission (in the afternoon). Inpatients, therefore, board in the ED, and the ED becomes overcrowded.

- There is a shortage of nurses and physicians. Hospital units and ED beds remain closed for want of staff, and the ED becomes overcrowded.

- A hospital's nearby competitor goes out of business. The demand for care suddenly increases and its inpatient beds fill up. The ED becomes overcrowded.

- A community has a shortage of primary care physicians. Preventive and early care is less available, and the demand for urgent care rises. The ED becomes overcrowded.

- A community's mental health network is inadequate. Patients requiring mental health hospitalization have nowhere to go. Patients in behavioral crisis are brought to the ED where they wait for a bed. The ED becomes overcrowded.

No matter what the health care problem, the result seems to be an overcrowded ED. Long waits and overcrowded EDs compromise not only quality, but patient safety. Delays in care likewise increase the hospital's exposure to professional liability claims and regulatory sanctions.

The impact of ED overcrowding on patient safety

An overcrowded ED clearly poses a problem to the hospital. Unless we're on the hospital board of trustees, why should we care?

For one thing, an overcrowded ED makes life in the surrounding community more risky. Here are some scenarios that ED nurses and physicians will recognize:

- A family brings a patient with abdominal pain to the ED. The waiting room is filled beyond capacity. There are 10 admitted patients waiting for a hospital bed inside the ED. Although the triage nurses are working as quickly as they can, it is 30 minutes before an assessment begins. The patient is assigned to the "Urgent" triage category, and although he does not appear to have a life-threatening condition, he needs a gurney for his physician examination (medical screening). The triage nurse believes the problem to be gastroenteritis, but the physician will perform a thorough diagnostic work up after the patient is sent to the back. The patient waits quietly and uncomfortably in the corner of the waiting room for his turn. Two hours later he is placed in a gurney inside the main ED. After another 45 minutes, the physician finally begins an exam, orders a STAT abdominal computed tomography (CT) scan, and discovers a dissecting aortic aneurysm.

- A patient with coronary heart disease is worked up in the ED. It is decided that she should be admitted for treatment. Because a bed is not available, she is boarded in the ED for 12 hours. The patient is in borderline critical condition, and the doctor orders intravenous drips and a complex of medications. Were the patient in the intensive care unit (ICU), she would have 1:2 nurse staffing. Because she is in a busy ED, however, nursing resources are torn between caring for her and assessing and caring for the flood of incoming patients. Staff are as attentive as possible, but their attention is diverted by the needs of other patients.

- A 65-year-old man experiences chest pain at home. His wife calls 911. Paramedics respond within 15 minutes, but the patient cannot be transported to the ED for another hour because all critical care ambulances are tied up at hospital EDs, waiting to offload their patients.

Stories similar to these and worse happen hundreds of times each day. In emergency medicine, timeliness is quality. The timeliness of medical screening, thrombelytic therapy, and trauma care directly affects clinical outcomes. Overcrowded EDs, therefore, clearly adversely impact patient safety and the timeliness (read: quality) of emergency care.

Impact of ED overcrowding on compliance

Legislators react to such issues as the acute care crisis in predictable ways: They pass laws to fix the problem by fiat. A perfect example is the federal Emergency Medical Treatment and Active Labor Act, or EMTALA.[1] These federal regulations go far beyond the original intent, which was to ensure that physicians and hospitals do not perform "wallet biopsies" on patients at the threshold of the ED. Over the past decade, EMTALA has grown into the quintessential ED quality regulation.

EMTALA requires that all patients receive a medical screening examination (by a physician, physician assistant, etc.) and stabilizing care regardless of ability to pay. EMTALA citations, however, have also been issued under the following circumstances:

- Patients leave of their own accord prior to medical screening because of "excessive" delays.
- Physicians miss a diagnosis.
- On-call consultants fail to respond.
- Is this extension of EMTALA into quality control a bad thing?

At the risk of raising the ire of our readers, we believe it to be just fine. In some health care systems, EMTALA has been necessary to raise the sensitivity of the organization to fundamental operational and quality concerns. Although EMTALA vulnerability can never be completely eliminated, some systems have spent productive resources on improving ED and hospital operations because of persistent EMTALA concerns.

---

[1] For complete information about EMTALA, visit the CMS web site at http://cms/hhs.gov/.

Other regulatory agencies are having their say as well. Managed health care regulators point to clogged EDs in the network as access problems for the HMO. Due to chronic high levels of diversion, Emergency Medical Systems (EMS) agencies have taken away hospital discretion in diverting ambulances. In addition, legislators have begun to specify nurse staffing ratios in the ED.

JCAHO's New Patient Flow Standard: LD.3.11[2]

A Tip About Tips: Throughout this book the authors offer "tips." This segment in particular salts tips among the formal requirements established by JCAHO. Please remember that a tip is just that: a thought stimulator; one way of doing things among many. Please don't make the mistake that many do: a tip is not a requirement … There are as many ways to successfully comply with a JCAHO element of performance as there are institutions attempting to do so. So please take our tips as suggestions rather than requirements.

In February 2004 the Joint Commission on Accreditation of Healthcare Organizations (JCAHO) published a new standard to address the hospital overcrowding crisis. JCAHO adopted this new standard, tentatively named LD.3.11, in recognition of the potential effect of overcrowding on patient safety and quality of care.

The initial draft of the standard proposed the complete prohibition of the practice of "boarding" patients in the emergency department. (A patient is "boarded" when they remain in the emergency department for a significant period of time after admission to inpatient status. Some hospitals consider any patient remaining in the ED longer than an hour past the admission order to be a "boarder." Other hospitals set the trigger for boarder status at two hours.)

After significant pushback from the hospital industry, the JCAHO reconsidered, apparently realizing that establishing a *per ser* prohibition against ED boarding was not realistic in the face of rampant overcrowding. While the final standard struck a better balance between the ideal and the achievable, it was not met with universal praise. In the February 9, 2004 edition, of *Modern Health Care* Dr. J. Brian Hancock, President, American College of Emergency Physicians, wrote "The Joint Commission had an opportunity to take a major step forward in eliminating a problem, and they fell short."

Such concerns not withstanding, the process outlined in JCAHO's standard is very consistent with proven approaches to the hospital crowding crisis and fits very nicely with the approaches suggested in this book.

---

[2] *For up-to-date information and complete text of the JCAHO standards, visit www.jcaho.org.*

Here is the JCAHO's new standard:

Standard LD.3.11: The leaders devise and implement plans for identifying and alleviating impediments to efficient patient flow throughout the organization.

The JCAHO's new scoring method provides for the "indirect" scoring of standards: Each standard is evaluated indirectly through the scoring of individual "elements of performance" (EP).

Elements of Performance for LD.3.11

The only part of the standard that is subject to specific "scoring" or enforcement by JCAHO are the following "elements of performance."

EP.1. Leaders investigate the organization's patient flow issues and their effect on patient safety and devise plans to alleviate that effect.

The focus of this book is summarized in this single element of performance. The intent of this very straightforward requirement is powerful: Leaders must truly understand the processes that contribute to problems in patient flow so they can improve flow and protect patients.

Although JCAHO and the surveyors that represent it are in the wrong position to judge the quality of such assessments, we are convinced that an objective, accurate, and focused look at the level of functioning of the various patient flow processes is essential. It not only is the first step in the journey to improved quality of care, it also is fundamental to ensuring the continued financial wellbeing of the institution.

Tip: Use this book as a guide for a patient flow assessment. Evaluate your hospital's performance against the "successful approaches" detailed throughout this book.

EP.2. Planning includes the delivery of necessary care to admitted patients who are held in temporary bed areas, e.g. Emergency Department area.

Patients in crowded hospitals are frequently held for extended periods in temporary beds. They often languish in a location whose architectural design and clinical systems are better suited to quick turnaround rather than ongoing observation and therapy. JCAHO singles out the ED and post anesthesia recovery units for special mention. After all, it is only natural that paramedic patients will remain in the ED until a bed is available and surgery patients will remain in the PACU following surgery.

Even though the ED and PACU are natural and traditional locations for temporary beds, care processes used in these areas are not always equivalent to inpatient systems. Take the system for medication management as an example. Most EDs and PACUs are considered "physician-controlled environments" and do not require the involvement of pharmacy in the review of medication orders (the source of over half of all adverse medication events). Yet the pharmacist's pre-administration review is required once a patient is admitted. JCAHO now requires evidence that this and many other patient safety/quality of care concerns are accounted for when patient boarding becomes necessary.

Tip: When conducting the patient flow assessment, study the differences in clinical processes for admitted patients in the intensive care, telemetry, or medical surgical units and the processes used to care for patients held in ED or PACU (staffing levels, qualifications, medications processes, etc.). Then, seek to establish equivalent processes for inpatients boarded in ED and PACU.

Tip: Consider staffing "boarders" with inpatient nurses who have been oriented to the unit (ED or PACU). This will ensure that the nurse has familiarity with inpatient processes, which will "jump start" the admission assessment process and will accommodate the differences in mindset that often exist between inpatient and ED or PACU nursing personnel.

Tip: Why "board" the patient in the ED or PACU at all? More and more hospitals are using temporary locations on the inpatient unit for patients awaiting a bed. Implementing such a system has two benefits: It motivates inpatient nursing to open another bed and it puts the patient in an environment where normal inpatient safeguards are natural.

> EP.3. Leaders and medical staff work together to create methods that promote efficient patient flow.

This EP recognizes the unfortunate fact that not all hospitals and their medical staffs enjoy a collegial and collaborative relationship. JCAHO therefore underscores the need to enlist the physician organization in the effort to improve patient flow.

Tip: Show evidence that the patient flow assessment performed as a result of EP.1 is presented at the medical executive committee.

Tip: Enlist a physician leader (preferably from the non-emergency medicine attending staff) to champion flow improvements.

EP.4. Planning encompasses the delivery of necessary care and services to patients placed in overflow areas, such as hallways.

This requirement is only subtly different than EP.2 (which addresses boarded patients). EP.4 requires the hospital to develop practices that ensure patients are given equivalent care whether they are located in an official bed space or in the hallway.

Tip: List hallway beds on the patient assignment/white board.

Tip: Use privacy screens to protect the hallway patient's privacy and dignity.

Tip: Set criteria for which patients are appropriate for hallway beds and which must be cared for in a standard treatment area.

EP.5. The organization uses specific indicators to measure the patient flow process's components. These measures include:

    a. Patient bed space supply
    b. Patient care and treatment areas efficiency
    c. Patient care and treatment areas safety
    d. Support service procedures that affect patient flow.

EP.6. Organization provides indicator results to staff members who are responsible for systems that support patient flow.

EP.7. Leadership receives regular reports on indicator results to support planning.

These three requirements form the basis of balanced scorecards, which we discuss in more detail elsewhere in this book. Even more than the assessment, establishing and holding people accountable for their performance based on the right data is the feature that distinguishes successful improvement efforts from expensive failures.

Tip: Make each scorecard no more than one page.

Tip: The indicators display should track performance on a monthly basis across the page.

Tip: Consider creating a spider chart showing performance.

Tip: There should be a leadership or oversight "patient flow" scorecard and a scorecard for each involved hospital department (inpatient nursing, admitting, housekeeping, clinical laboratory, radiology, etc.).

Tip: The leadership/oversight scorecard should focus on overall indicators of flow performance. It is not practical to have all department indicators reported on the oversight scorecard. To meet the requirements of EP.7, list the macroflow indicators (left without being seen, wait times for ED care, diversions, number of boarders, admit times, average time of day of discharge, etc.) and also list which departments are meeting and not meeting their individual performance thresholds. Leadership should have individual departmental scorecards available to them should they wish to delve further.

Tip: Include overall measures of performance, not just measures that relate to patient flow, in the departmental scorecard.

Tip: Scorecard content should be driven by those indicators that are important to leadership—not those things important to JCAHO.

Tip: Don't forget to incorporate safety (e.g., listings of adverse events that may be related to patient flow problems) and bed availability.

EP.8. The organization improves dangerous or ineffective practices that are deemed essential to patient flow by leaders.

Attention: JCAHO is actually requiring improvement— not just attempts to improve. That is what this book is all about—real improvement.

Tip: Read, understand, and use this book.

Tip: Focus on the issue that is truly important to leadership.

Tip: Connect improvement targets with Return on Investment to ensure appropriate funding.

EP.9. The organization defines criteria for initiating diversion.

It is surprising that relatively few emergency departments actually have written and enforced diversion criteria. The GAO's study mentioned earlier demonstrates significant variability between the local EMS agencies as to how and when paramedics are diverted. However, it behooves the hospital to have consistent criteria for when diversion is initiated and when diversion is terminated.

Since the ambulatory and inpatient flows tend to be separate (discussed in subsequent sections), the criteria should be focused on the gurney area (the "main ED") rather than the waiting room.

These criteria will be highly individual but should be very objective. For example, some EMS agencies have a category of "neurological diversion" when the CT scanner is down.

Here's a start on criteria for saturation diversion:

- Diversion for saturation may be initiated by the charge nurse with the approval of the physician in charge and the administrator on call. Except in extreme situations, approval of the administrator on call is required prior to the initiation of diversion. Approval of the physician in charge is always required prior to the initiation of diversion.

- Staffing saturation: The charge nurse shall initiate saturation diversion whenever there are insufficient physician or nursing staff to safely care for the patients on hand. This will always involve a collaborative judgment between nursing and emergency medicine. However, the following are indicators of potential staffing issues:

  - "Urgent" patients are waiting more than an hour after bed placement for a physician examination.

  - Patients must wait more than a half hour for a nursing assessment after bed placement.

(Please remember, these are examples only. In the real world, arriving at criteria for staffing saturation is very difficult. That is why most saturation is initiated solely on space availability.)

- Physical saturation: The charge nurse shall recommend saturation diversion to the physician in charge and administration whenever

    - all beds and temporary gurney spaces in the main ED are occupied by patients (unless the patient is about to be transferred to another unit), and

    - all alternatives for "boarding" patients in other units have been exhausted.

- Termination of Diversion Status: The charge nurse shall reevaluate continued diversion at least every 30 minutes and shall terminate diversion, after consultation with the physician in charge, once the justifying criteria are no longer met.

The impact of ED overcrowding on hospital cash flow

Today's ED is the front door to most hospitals. For a hospital to close its ED is a sign of significant stress. Yet this front door is often seen as a money loser.

The ED actually loses money on the average ED visit ($84 loss per visit, up from a $46 loss in a recent California study[3]).

However, the hospital makes money on each inpatient admission ($1200 per admission). Patients admitted through the ED generated 20% of the hospital's net profit in the same California study. These numbers vary greatly due to staffing ratios, payer mix, case mix, and cost of on-call physicians.

Given this backdrop, how does an overcrowded ED hurt the hospital's bottom line?

- Potential admissions are diverted to other institutions
- Inpatients are held in the highest-cost location—the ED—for an extended period of time
- Opportunities are lost for effective case management and discharge planning
- Ancillary consultations are delayed, extending the length of stay
- Observation stays (fixed charge) are unnecessarily extended, driving up costs without increasing revenue

---

[3] *California Healthcare Foundation, Profitability, July 2003.*

A better understanding of ED overcrowding

A hospital we knew believed it did not have the physical capacity to care for all of the ambulatory patients presenting to its ED. Leadership believed its high number of paramedic diversion hours to be evidence of this lack of capacity. When compliance concerns caused the institution to discontinue its years-long practice of triaging patients into nearby medical offices, executive leadership believed that diversions would balloon.

A year later, after close attention to "front end" ED processes, wait times for bed placement in ED were steadily decreasing and left-without-being-seen (LWBS) rates declined as satisfaction increased. To the surprise of some, diversion rates were unaffected by the increase in patient volume caused by the regulatory concern.

Why didn't increasing volume to an already stressed ED system increase the tendency to divert paramedic runs? Because paramedic traffic and ambulatory patients feed separate ED flows. (Exhibit I.1)

Two separate and distinct patient flows

EDs have two distinct patient flow patterns:

- Ambulatory care
- High-acuity care

Most high-acuity patients arrive through the ambulance entrance. High numbers of paramedic diversions are due to a lack of effectiveness in the high-acuity patient flow.

Most ambulatory patients arrive through the front door. Poor patient satisfaction and high LWBS rates are related to dysfunction in the ambulatory care patient flow. (see Exhibits I.1 and I.2.)

Exhibit I.1

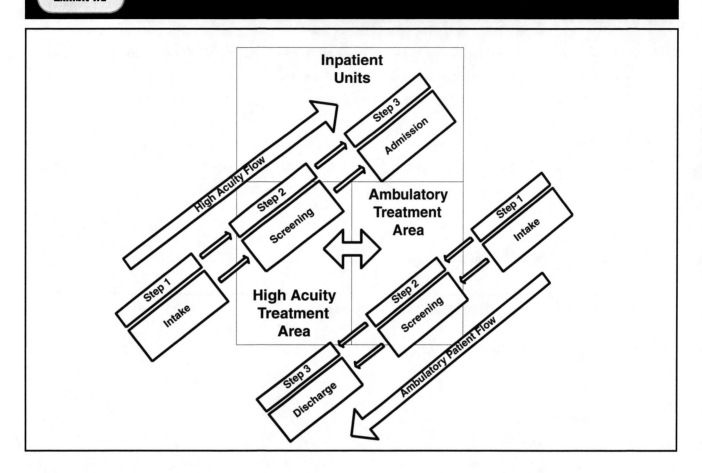

Ambulatory care

Question: Why do patients have a low opinion of an ED?

Answer: Because of long waits for ambulatory care. A recent study found that 47% of patients who leave without being seen do so because the wait is too long. An additional 38% left because there appeared to be a lengthy wait.[4]

The overcrowded waiting room is a symptom of a dysfunctional ambulatory care patient flow. Therefore, if the issue prompting the change effort is patient satisfaction or delays in the medical screening of ambulato-

---

[4] Arendt, K. Annals of Emergency Medicine. September 2003, 43(3), pp 317-323.

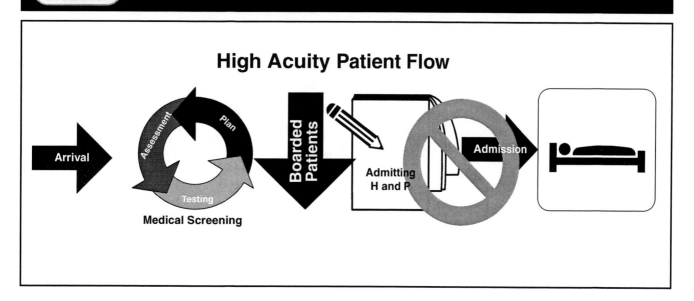

ry patients, the focus of improvement should be the functional capacity of the ambulatory patient flow. The hospital could successfully focus on the following:

- Triage staffing
- Intake processes
- Triage systems and competencies
- Enhancement of ambulatory care locations and models

High acuity care: Paramedic diversions and patient boarding

Question: Why do EDs go on diversion?
Answer: Because all staffed gurney spaces in the ED are occupied.

Question: Why are all available ED gurney spaces occupied?
Answer: Because the functional capacity of the inpatient system is inadequate.

Between 1990 and 2000, the total number of ED treatment spaces increased in California. The number of patients and severity of their ailments also increased. Even with these developments, however, the number of staffed critical care beds decreased in that time period.[5] With more patients and fewer beds to put them in, California EDs were forced to divert an increasing number of paramedic ambulances.

---

[5] California Health Care Foundation. California's Emergency Department: System Capacity and Demand. March 2003.

Because not every ED has this option, measuring the number of diversion hours has significant limitations. It may be better to measure the number of "boarded patients" if high acuity patient flow is the problem.

Boarded patients are individuals who have been admitted to the hospital for an inpatient or observation stay but who must wait in the ED because there is no available inpatient or observation[6] bed. Schneider, et al,[7] polled 90 hospital EDs on Monday evening, March 7, 2001. One hundred percent of the treatment spaces in these departments were occupied. Seventy-three percent of the departments were boarding two or more inpatients. Yet only 11% of EDs were diverting ambulances, even though most were using hallway or other "temporary beds" and about half felt they had insufficient nursing staff to care for the patient load.

Boarding inpatients and observation patients is therefore a significant contributor to ED overcrowding. Researchers found that patients waiting in the ED for consultation by on-call physicians accounted for 7.6% of ED patients. Thirty-six percent of EDs contacted had two or more patients waiting for consultants.

There are a number of approaches to making improvements in this area. One could choose to address issues such as the following:

- Streamline the admitting history and physical process
- Improve the ED to inpatient nursing report process
- Decrease bed turnaround time
- Optimize patient discharges
- Reduce overall length of stay

How to eat an elephant

For those of you familiar with time management principles, the concept of eating an elephant is familiar.[8] It goes something like this:

Question: "How do you eat an elephant?"
Answer: "One meal at a time."

At the risk of offending People for the Ethical Treatment of Animals (PETA), the analogy is apt. Solving the health care crisis is very much like eating an elephant. The task is too big to be tackled—or even understood—all at once. Instead, one must examine the puzzle piece by piece.

---

[6] Observation status, prompted by Medicare reimbursement rules, is a short inpatient-like stay. Most observation patients stay for under 24 hours, although some remain in observation status for 48 or more.
[7] Schneider, Sandra. "Emergency Department Crowding: A Point in Time." Annals of Emergency Medicine. August 2003.
[8] Author Steven Covey uses this metaphor extensively in his popular works on time management and personal productivity.

Six subprocesses

To address an ED in crisis—"the elephant"—begin by dividing the beast into understandable (digestible) parts. We, like many before us, have chosen to define six "subprocesses" of care.

The first three subprocesses are components of the ED flow. The last three subprocesses are components of inpatient flow. All six subprocesses, which we will discuss in the remainder of this book, include:

- ED intake
- ED throughput
- ED output
- Inpatient intake
- Inpatient throughput
- Inpatient output

Each of these subprocesses has customers and suppliers. The nature of the customers and the performance of the suppliers impacts the performance of the subprocess.

ED intake

The first subprocess is very complex and problem prone. ED intake includes:

- Arrival
- Registration
- Triage
- Waiting
- Observation and reassessment
- Bed placement

There is significant variation from hospital to hospital in this subprocess, and we will devote a number of pages to each of the practices that have proven effective in optimizing the ED intake subprocess.

You may have heard about the "triage push" system or the "ED pull" approach. All these and others have huge potential in decreasing the wait times for care.

If your problem is dissatisfied customers and patients who leave without being seen, spending time on the intake subprocess should be well worth your while.

ED throughput

ED throughput is also known in EMTALA circles as the "medical screening" process. It begins with the initial physician (or allied health professional) examination and often involves laboratory tests and imaging studies.

Improving ED throughput is mostly about supplier performance. Improving supplier performance can improve ED throughput, which can impact the "functional capacity" of the department.

Throughput is normally measured as length of stay (LOS). However, some EDs also measure bed density (the number of patients seen per ED bed). Decreasing the amount of time a patient spends in an ED bed will increase the number of patients that may be seen in this bed. For example, decreasing the average ED LOS from four to three hours will increase the functional capacity of the ED by 33%. **This is equivalent to building an additional 10 beds onto a 30-bed ED.**

We will discuss successful approaches to making this magnitude of improvement in the ED throughput subprocess.

ED output

There are three major outputs for the ED: discharge, transfer, and admission. Admissions are obviously tied to the inpatient subprocesses. However, there is also much to be learned and improved about the discharge and transfer processes.

Inpatient intake

Otherwise known as the admitting process, inpatient intake is very complex, and is often complicated further by conflicting budgetary incentives. However, there have been many successful steps taken to improve this process. These include the following:

- Improving the bed management system
- Expediting the nursing report process
- Reducing budgetary disincentives
- Streamlining bed turnover activities

Inpatient throughput

This process is an "elephant" all by itself. Yet there is significant improvement possible through the implementation of robust case management and discharge planning programs. Many institutions are penny wise and pound (or perhaps ton) foolish by scrimping on these programs.

Case management is not simple. Institutions often give up when one attempt at case management proves unsuccessful; but that, of course, is the wrong answer. A failed case management program ensures unnecessary and costly stays that will only exacerbate the emergency department crisis.

Inpatient output

One might think the inpatient discharge process was simple, but that's not true. Even though hospitals across the country have spent years focusing on the discharge process, few have it down to the science it can become.

As its name suggests, discharge planning can be an important contributor to resolution of this issue, as are hundreds of seemingly little things, such as transportation, wheelchair access, and nursing assignments.

A word about improving

Knowing what's wrong and making it better are two entirely different things. One can always find inspiring success stories about the various improvement approaches. Six Sigma, for example, is the current improvement favorite. This data-centric approach borrowed from manufacturing is, like other improvement approaches, very useful . . . sometimes.

Another such approach is Lean, which is even more appropriate for most emergency department flow problems. Developed by Toyota to improve assembly-line throughput, Lean is used to streamline processes. Many hospitals have used Lean techniques to improve hospital systems with very good results.

However, we've seen as many failures as successes with each of these processes. What at first appears to be a breakthrough often becomes a "Hawthorne" phenomenon. That's why the authors have developed a disciplined overlay to Six Sigma, Lean, and other improvement techniques. Called IDelta®, the improvement process begins by focusing on leadership's data and oversight processes. The success rate of improvement efforts can significantly increase if you apply the Plan-Do-Check-Act cycle of improvement to the data that will ultimately be used to judge the success or failure of the improvement process and to manage the day-to-day functions of the department.[9]

We have incorporated the IDelta® mindset into the benchmarks and improvements that constitute the body of this work.

---

[9] IDelta® is a product of InSight Advantage, LP, in Houston, Texas.

Critical element 1: Data
- Without accurate, timely administrative data, the manager is unable to manage and the institution is unable to improve.

Critical element 2: Routine visibility of results
- Frequent review of a few key performance indicators by senior leadership (e.g., a "patient flow dashboard") is essential for monitoring change.

Critical element 3: Unambiguous accountability
- The system at the focus of the improvement effort must have accurate data to measure the process that is frequently and conveniently available.

- The data must come to the routine attention of departmental and executive leadership.

- Clear, unambiguous accountabilities for performance in these data must be clearly established.

- Consider Lean to make processes efficient, rather than Six Sigma, which is more interested in reducing defects).

- Always be certain that the quality of care and service is not compromised in the name of efficiency.

SUBPROCESS 0

Leadership: The context for change

Subprocess 0

LEADERSHIP: THE CONTEXT FOR CHANGE

The first subprocess we'll discuss is actually not a subprocess at all; it's a superprocess, an overarching structure through which all other processes flow. It is leadership.

If you're an executive leader, you may feel the urge to skip to the next chapter—please don't! We won't be critical—we have found hospital leaders to be intelligent, well-meaning people trying to cope with an unmanageable challenge. However, we will discuss the tools and approaches leaders should adopt if they hope to make a dent in this daunting problem.

 Visibility and accountability

Before there can be a change to hospital overcrowding, the problem must be visible to senior leaders— very visible. Accountability for addressing the issue must be clear and unambiguous. Although most leaders will (at least privately) admit that hospital overcrowding is a problem, many are unable to definitively describe the extent or priority of the problem other than to quote paramedic diversion hours (perhaps the most idiosyncratic measure available).

YOU KNOW YOU NEED TO IMPROVE ED AND INPATIENT PROCESSES WHEN

- your "left without being seen" (LWBS) rate is climbing
- your patient, staff, and physician satisfaction is sinking
- you're on "diversion" at least part of every day
- inpatients are boarded every afternoon in the emergency department (ED)
- your ED is contributing less than 20% of your bottom line
- temporary bed spaces in the ED are always occupied

ARE YOU REALLY READY TO IMPROVE?

- Does executive leadership get regular reports on LWBS rate?
- Does the executive committee monitor your diversion rate?
- Are you measuring staff and physician satisfaction, or is patient satisfaction "good enough"?
- Has executive leadership resigned itself to the fact that the ED will always be a money loser?
- Does leadership take it for granted that patients will be boarded in the ED?

You hospital may have very severe overcrowding problems, but until the warning signs—measures of performance of the implicated processes—are high enough on leadership's worry list, you're not ready for change.

Putting data in front of leadership

Imagine running a department without a budget. Have you ever heard of a chief executive officer (CEO) who did not hold managers accountable for expenditures? How long would a manager or a chief financial officer (CFO) last if he or she did not know who was making money and who was losing money? It is unimaginable that anyone would run a hospital without income and expense data. No leader ever starts a year without a budget. No manager ever ends a year without a precise knowledge of his or her variance to that budget.

But how often is this tight monitoring of performance actually applied directly to operations? In other industries, this happens every day; in health care, it rarely happens.

Most of the time, vague, unreliable numbers about hospital systems performance are reported on a quarterly basis, if at all. Rarely are the numbers "actionable."

WHAT IS ACTIONABLE DATA?

As the name implies, actionable data is information on which sound business decisions may be based. It is

- reliable
- focused on the "right" part of the process
- reported frequently enough to be sensitive to change
- surrounded by supporting or normalizing information
- analyzed to be able to distinguish "noise" or normal variation from true change

---

There are good reasons for this lack of data:

- Health care is not the same as manufacturing telephones: It is easy to recognize a defective telephone but difficult to recognize a defective health care process.
- It is easy to measure the number of late widget shipments. Health care process data are, however, not traditionally collected (outside the clinical laboratory).
- Attempts to collect process data are often "trumped" by poor or inaccurate medical records documentation.
- There are not always convenient start and end points to health care processes.

There are many reasons that process data are not collected. However, until clinical process data are studied as closely as budget data, nothing will change.

We will discuss process data in more detail throughout the remainder of the book, but we will give you a quick list of common high-level process data related to hospital overcrowding:

- Patient left without being seen (LWBS) rate
- Monthly paramedic diversion hours
- Time from presentation to triage
- Duration of the triage assessment
- Time from presentation to provider (subdivided by triage acuity)
- ED length of stay for discharged patients
- ED length of stay for admitted patients
- Median number of boarded patients at 3:00 p.m., 6:00 p.m., and 9:00 p.m. (We define a "boarded" patient as one who remains in the ED one hour after inpatient's admission. Some may choose two hours as the trigger for boarding.)
- Length of stay from admission order to inpatient bed placement
- Patient satisfaction
- Staff turnover rate
- Staff vacancy rate
- Daily sick calls
- Percentage of admitted patients
- Percentage of "urgent" patients

Putting data into context

Measuring diversion rates in a vacuum gives you meaningless information. However, measuring diversion rates alongside the number of boarded patients creates a useful picture. Measuring LWBS rates can be helpful, too.

Better still is to cluster ED patient satisfaction, LWBS rate, time to provider for urgent patients, number of boarded patients, and time from admit order to inpatient bed placement. They all relate to one another. The cluster is greater than the sum of its parts.

Look at the example below in Exhibits 1.1 and 1.2:

Exhibit 1.1

Indicator	Jan	Feb	Mar	Apr
Percent left without being seen	3.5%	3.75%	4%	4.25%

Exhibit 1.2

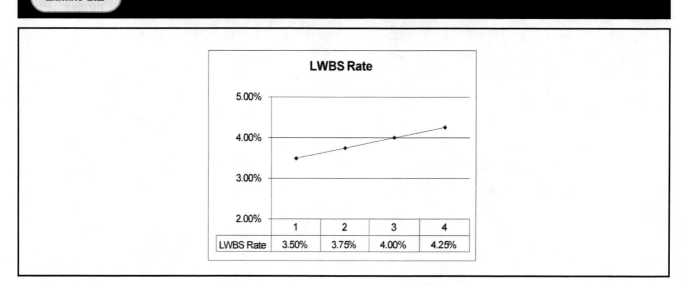

	1	2	3	4
LWBS Rate	3.50%	3.75%	4.00%	4.25%

With this data set, we've seen leaders take the "look and see" approach; the rate may just be varying randomly. In addition, if there is a problem, the data does not show what the problem is. However, what if the same data were reported alongside other supporting indicators as in Exhibits 1.3, 1.4, and 1.5?

Exhibit 1.3

Indicator	Jan	Feb	Mar	Apr
Percent left without being seen	3.5%	3.75%	4%	4.25%
Percent of patients highly satisfied with ED experience	70%	68%	66%	Pending
Minutes to provider for urgent patients	55	60	65	70

Exhibit 1.4

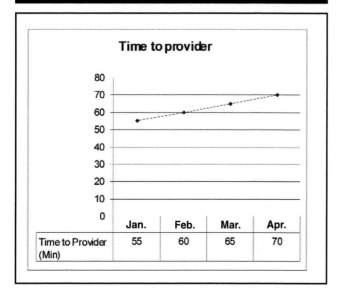

Exhibit 1.5

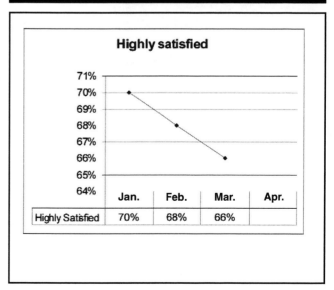

It's easy to see by glancing at this data that the ED is having front-end problems. This cluster of information speaks much more clearly than LWBS rates alone.

Report frequent data points

It's usually sufficient to report key monitoring data on a quarterly basis. However, the report should contain as many data points as are supported by the data collection method. All EDs can generate daily LWBS rates. But we often just look at them with monthly or quarterly averages. What a waste!

If you were to tell us that your LWBS rate for the quarter was 2%, we wouldn't know what to say. Is that good? Is that bad? However, if you were to give us a chart like Exhibit 1.6, we could all see in an instant that 2% was very good indeed.

Exhibit 1.6

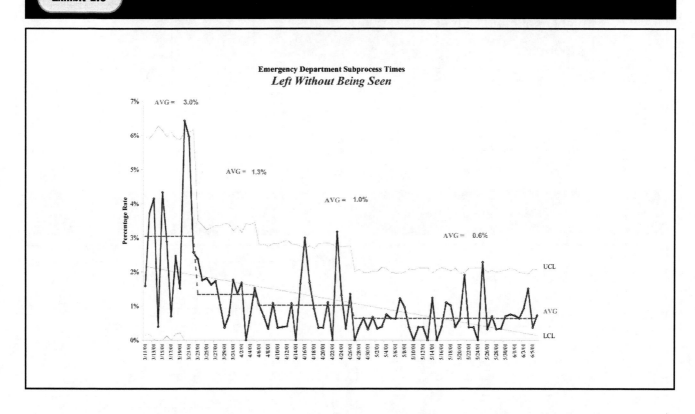

"But we don't have the time to collect all that data," you say. Wrong! The data for this display is exactly the same data it takes to give you a monthly rate. It is just displayed differently. The time commitment is in setting up the spreadsheet. Data entry amounts to entering two numbers a day: the number of patients who leave without being seen and the total volume of patients in the ED that day.

Make sure it's the right data

Sometimes hospitals report unreliable data. We have to admit to a pet peeve: We would rather see you report no data at all than inaccurate data.

Some hospitals are proud of their time-to-provider or patient satisfaction rate, only to find out that their satisfaction numbers were gathered from only 10 of the 3,000 patients who'd used their services for the quarter, or that the "provider examination time" was only recorded in the charts 10% of the time.

What to do? Just because important data is unreliable doesn't mean you shouldn't report it. To the contrary, having important data be unreliable is often a bigger problem than the data itself. In this situation, report on the reliability. Let's look at another example in Exhibit 1.7:

Exhibit 1.7

Indicator	Jan	Feb	Mar	Apr
Minutes to provider examination for "urgent" patients	60	65	63	70
Percent data capture: "Time of provider exam"	10%	15%	20%	25%
Percent data capture: "Triage category"	55%	60%	65%	70%

It looks like the time-to-provider rate is going the wrong way. But is this really a bad report? We argue that this is a positive report. The data capture is steadily rising, showing that the manager has been paying attention to the seemingly simple but actually complex problem of collecting the correct data. Soon there may be a high enough sample to actually concentrate on improving "minutes to provider examination."

Accountability

Accountability for improvement must be clear and unambiguous for things to change. However, this is often easier said than done. For example, who should be accountable for improving data capture for time to provider? The usual reaction is to make nursing responsible for this data collection issue. However, it's often a physician documentation problem. Making nursing accountable forces staff to try to pay attention to the precise moment the physician begins his or her examination. This doesn't garner a positive response.

A better tactic would be to realize that it's a physician's responsibility. In the ED, it is usually possible to get the contract group to cooperate in collecting the data. However, if you really want to improve, make the contract group accountable. Negotiate a penalty for poor data capture into the contract.

It sounds easy, but we know it's not. This means that you'll have to prioritize your issues. This can be done only after you make certain that you know what you're trying to accomplish.

Take aim on the right improvement target

If you try to do everything at once, you'll accomplish nothing. Study long and hard before you choose whether to address hospital overcrowding. Is it really that important to you? Ask yourself the following:

- How much will solving this contribute to the bottom line?
- Which customers am I trying to satisfy by addressing this issue?
- Where does this fit on the board's priority list?

Once you're convinced overcrowding is the issue, you must decide which part of the problem you want to address. That's where an expert, in-depth assessment comes in handy.

What? Spend money on a consultant just to tell me what I already know? Although consultants love to have the business, there is another way. Ask your staff. If you read and understand the potential for performance with each of the subprocesses in this book, you can get a good list of what you're not doing that could affect overcrowding. That's about the best assessment you could ever perform. It may take some time, but it is quite possible for you to make a list of all the best practices in this book, compare your practices against this best practice list, prioritize this gap analysis against those practices that would have the largest impact on performance, and choose your target for performance improvement.

Seeking nirvana

If you've been paying attention to the literature or going to the seminars, you've heard about incredible improvements made by very talented people. Although most of the "seminar ideas" sound great, few have taken hold across the industry. Once there is a critical mass—once the industry is in enough pain—some of these grand sweeping changes will become commonplace. Let's take a brief look at the sweeping approaches that may be paving the way for the rest of us.

⊖ Tiered, triggered response systems

CONSIDER THIS WHEN:

- the hospital has robust, reliable real-time information systems for all key indicators
- the hospital has an established performance improvement culture
- ED/hospital overcrowding is top on the hospital's priority list

A tiered, triggered response system is a set of measures with set responses as the measures go from good to bad.

Example #1: Simple

One of the best practices we describe in the body of the book is a trigger for "virtual fast track." The trigger could be **when there are six or more combined nonurgent and minor patients waiting for longer than one hour. The lead triage nurse will then be freed up to work with one of the emergency medicine physicians to disposition the patients.** This is the simplest form of triggered response: The trigger is objective, and the actions are concrete. This triggered response process increases the functional capacity of the department as necessary to meet the fluctuating demand for fast-track services, thereby improving patient flow.

Example #2: Complex

Overlook Hospital in New Jersey has been a leader in developing this innovative approach. The following is an example of the type of system that can be implemented, based loosely on the Overlook Hospital experience. It is not intended to precisely reflect their actual process.

The hospital has an electronic patient-tracking system that provides a real-time display of selected critical hospital processes (ED throughput, inpatient capacity, laboratory turnaround, radiology turnaround, etc.). The graphs are displayed at the nursing stations of the ED, in the ED manager's office, and on the desk of the CEO. The status of each process is displayed as an electronic run chart (a line graph over time). Goal lines are set for each process, and the data is displayed in 15-minute averages. Current performance is displayed as the last point: The prior three hours of data are displayed as the prior 12 data points. Interventions are triggered when there are three data points that exceed the threshold for the measured process.

The graphical display illustrated in Exhibit 1.8 changes shades as the condition of the process deteriorates, allowing staff and leaders to quickly identify a system in trouble. The processes measured are given white, gray, and black designations.

Exhibit 1.8

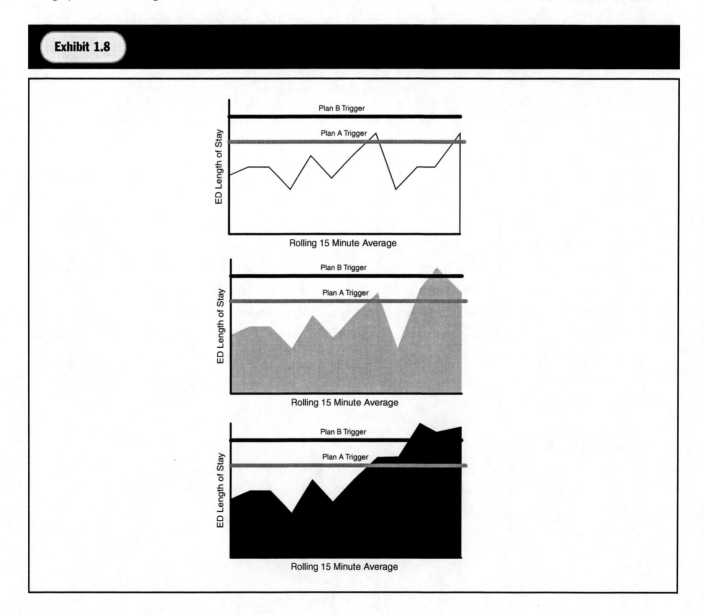

WHITE: A very good day. When there are no patients waiting too long for service. No interventions are required to facilitate safe and efficient patient flow. **Managers want their systems to stay white.**

GRAY: A system in distress and mandated responses are triggered. Early actions are initiated to prevent impending gridlock. For example, managers become directly involved in managing patient flow or delivering care; resources are diverted from noncritical tasks, physicians are asked to discharge their patients earlier (as appropriate), etc.

BLACK: A gridlocked system with meltdown impending. Aggressive actions are triggered. Staff are called to duty from home, physicians are required to round early in the most critical areas, and elective surgeries and admissions are postponed.

Begin where the light is shining

On his way home one overcast night, a man came across the dim figure of a boy pawing at the ground under a lonely street lamp. The man said, "It's awfully late, son. Don't you think you should go home?"

"But I have to find my mother's keys. I dropped them and I can't go home until I find them," the boy replied.

"Let me help," said the man as he got down on his hands and knees under the glow of the street lamp. After a few minutes, both the boy and the man had covered every inch of pavement three times over with no luck.

"I don't know what to tell you, son . . . your mother's keys just don't seem to be here."

"I guess I'm not surprised," said the boy. "I actually dropped them way back over there," pointing.

"Then why have we been looking here?" asked the man.

"Because this is where the light is shining," replied the boy.

Not a terribly funny joke, but one of our favorites. It reminds us of two things:

- We tend to look at and improve those things that are illuminated by data
- We need to take advantage of serendipity

A hospital is an organic thing

It is good to remind ourselves that health care is an organization on its head. Out of habit, we tend to believe that there is a CEO who is really in charge, with direct reports who have direct reports, who, in turn, have direct reports, and so forth until every position in the organization is accounted for. It's the typical "command and control" paradigm.

The command and control approach works (or at least we thought it did) for most industries. If you were making widgets, you could do so with a grand widgeteer entrepreneur at the top of the organization, five deputy widgeteers (for widget sales, manufacturing, human resources, financial operations, and staff functions), 25 assistant deputy widgeteers, etc.

The difference in the hospital business is that, for the most part, the customer is not the patient. The customer is, rather, the physician: a licensed, very independent practitioner. We can hear many protesting now that the customer is the patient. In many ways, of course, that is correct. But we prefer to think of it a little differently

- the product: high-quality, efficient patient care
- the customer: the attending physician who is acting on behalf of the patient

Why is that important? Because flowing change through a system where the physician is both a part of the system and the primary customer of the system is difficult. (See Exhibit 1.9.) It definitely calls the "command and control" paradigm into question.

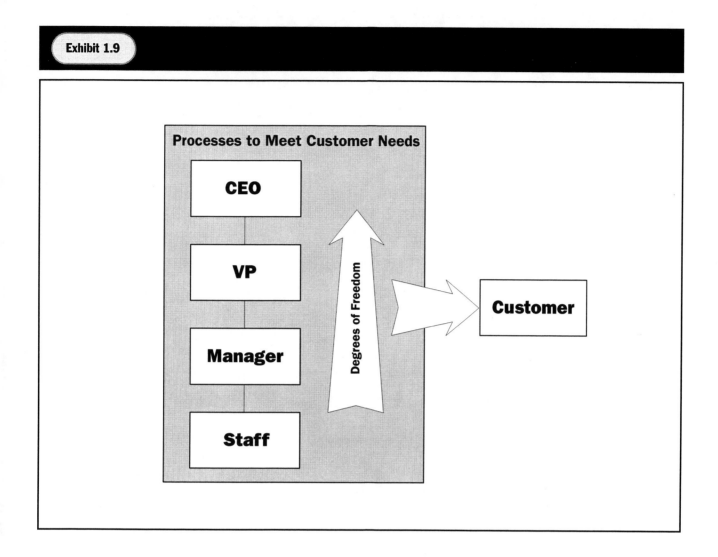

Exhibit 1.9

Processes to Meet Customer Needs

CEO

VP

Manager

Staff

Degrees of Freedom

Customer

Budgeting and economics

It is important that one learns and studies the budgeting process as one plans to improve hospital flow. To truly understand a health care process, one must understand who wins and who loses in the current system, and must make sure that the new and improved system does not cause disadvantage for important players such as the physician or the nurse executive.

Penalties for opening available inpatient beds

Everybody wins when we have a bed for the patient, right? Not necessarily. We hope the hospital wins, but that does not necessarily mean that all the players in the hospital do. Many hospital budgeting systems result in a system of barriers between nursing managers and moving patients through the hospital. Here's how it often works.

Nursing is a hospital's largest operational expense. The nurse executive is pressed by the CFO to keep the nursing budget in line—to come in under target, if at all possible. The nurse executive naturally holds the various nurse managers to their budget (total dollars and hours per patient day). What, then, will affect the nurse manager's success?

A nursing unit will incur expenses if it staffs more beds than planned, calls in staff in the middle of a shift, or frequently sends staff home in the middle of a shift.

Another problem is that it's truly impossible to tell objectively whether you have the right number of nurses on a unit. Consultants can always come into a unit and theorize that operations can be accomplished with fewer staff. Managers will always worry that cutting staff will compromise quality. We also know that cutting staff can lead to poor nursing satisfaction and high turnover rates. It's one of the many catch-22 scenarios in health care:

- If nurse staffing is too rich, the hospital will suffer from excessive costs.
- If nurse staffing is too lean, quality and satisfaction suffer, patients stay in the bed longer, and the hospital suffers from excessive costs.

The discussion between nursing and finance generally sounds like this:

"My patients have a higher acuity [need more services] than the budget allows," says the nurse executive.

"If that's true, why hasn't my billable case mix changed?" asks the CFO.

What does this dynamic do to hospital throughput? It puts kinks in the system.

Units and beds remain closed. Patients stay in the ED until the next shift or until a staffed bed opens. It is what you would expect when a system with variable demand (health care in general and EDs in particular) meets a system with fixed capacity that is trying to function with all staffed beds filled. We know that the demand of hospitalization is exceedingly variable (refer to the discussions of "smoothing" on p. 22). Yet, nursing units are most efficient (and nurse managers are most happy) when the hospital is operating with all of its planned, staffed beds filled (and not a single patient more). If a manager is budgeted for 100 medical/surgical beds at acuity 3, that's exactly what the manager wants to have. Predictability equals manageability. Partially filled units mean increases in cost per patient day.

In a normal hospital, the nurse manager has two options:

- Be a team player, be quick to bring in extra staff, and get blamed for going over budget
- Stay in the good graces of the CFO and let the extra patients stay in the ED or ICU until an already open bed becomes available

The trick is that the CFO and CEO must develop a system that looks at the big picture. Otherwise, even though the nurse manager in the example above will stay within budget, the hospital will lose money.

Approaches:

- Plan for a large, cross-trained float pool. Nurse managers would not be "charged" for taking from the pool.
- Avoid unnecessary specialty units to allow more bed placement flexibility.
- Invest in staffing tools and incentives in addition to hours per patient day.
- Implement a reporting and accountability system for daily monitoring at various levels of the organization.
- Apply the performance improvement process to budgeting, with the goal of increasing admissions without adversely affecting any manager's budget.

This is a tough problem to solve, but the result should be a flexible capacity that can quickly expand to accommodate routine fluctuations in demand. (Of course, decreasing variability in demand for such things as elective surgery is also a useful and effective approach.)

Shifting costs to the ED

Although boarding patients in the ED creates a number of problems—both economic and operational—for the hospital, it can ripple false incentives through nursing middle management.

- The revenue for inpatient admissions accrues to the inpatient manager's budget, including the entire income for patients who boarded in the ED for part of their stay
- The cost of the "boarded" care given accrues to the ED

Data, Data, Data

CONSIDER THIS WHEN:

Always.

We've probably already made our point about the importance of data, but you'll continue to hear about it as we go.

That graph makes my hair hurt!

A true story:

While working with an ED manager recently, we tried to explain the backup in the waiting room in graphical terms. We used a scatter graph to show something the manager already knew: People wait longer at certain points in the day. Even though the manager recognized the problem, there was no evidence that the manager was adjusting processes to deal with it. Why? Because like many clinical people, the manager did not understand how to use and analyze data.

Around the same time, we tried to convince a senior leader of a multihospital system that the ED managers needed education in data analysis. The senior leader did not accept the suggestion. Why? Been there, done that! There is often a huge disconnect between training on Demming's statistical process control methods and the realities of daily life in the trenches. Clinical management often does much more putting out fires than process improvement. Worse, all the data analysis tools in the world are meaningless when used to analyze data that is inaccurate, incomplete, or beside the point.

The path to systems salvation, then, begins with collecting accurate and complete data about the right part of the system.

Accurate data: Without data quality control there is no data quality

One multihospital system we worked with had a robust admission, discharge, and transfer data (ADT) computer system. It had more than 100 data elements related to a typical ED stay. It was also used to transmit orders from the nursing station to the laboratory, radiology, and pharmacy.

What a wealth of data! Yes and no.

Data that was collected as a natural part of the clinical process (orders for test, request for beds) was present and accurate.

Data collected that was not part of the clinical process, however, was inaccurate or nonexistent:

- We knew when the bed was ordered, but we didn't know when the patient actually left the unit
- We knew when the patient was registered, but we didn't know when he or she was seen by a physician

True, there were numbers in the computer system, but many did not correspond with what actually was happening.

In another example, we were surprised to learn of the high number of emergent patients seen in one department. At first we thought, "Boy, these folks are taking care of really sick patients." On closer inspection, however, we learned that the clerk responsible for entering the triage category did not have a copy of the nursing triage form—the only place the triage category was recorded. The clerk had to guess at the triage category.

Successful approaches

You may have hundreds of data points and, yes, half of them are garbage, but most of those inaccurate data points are really not essential.

First decide which data elements are truly critical to measuring the process in question. Keep the number of important data elements down to a precious few.

Next develop a quality control system. Make a specific individual accountable for measuring and reporting the accuracy of the data selected elements. This should become a routine accountability. Responsibility for the integrity of the data entered into the critical elements should be clear. The person collecting the quality control (QC) data should be someone other than the person responsible for entering the data.

Example:

Assume the problem that you are addressing is the length of stay for nonurgent and minor patients.

Flow-chart the process and find the following potential checkpoints (shown in Exhibit 1.10):
You are tempted to do what you've always done and simply examine lab turnaround time. That's where the light is already shining. You have #10 and #11. They're accurate. Let's measure it!

Exhibit 1.10

#	Data element	☺☺☹	Status
1	Time of arrival	☹	Not captured ("data capture" refers to collection of the data in the automated data system).
2	Time of registration	☺	Accurate and always captured.
3	Time of triage start	☹	Not captured. Not documented in the medical record.
4	Time to triage end	☺	Not captured. Documented in the medical record some of the time.
5	Triage category	☺	Captured but not accurate.
6	Time to waiting room	☹	Not captured. Not documented in the medical record.
7	Time of waiting reassessment	☹	Not captured. Sometimes documented in the medical record.
8	Time of bed placement	☺	Captured but inaccurate.
9	Time of first provider exam	☹	Not captured. Sometimes documented in the medical record.
10	Time of lab order	☺	Accurate and always captured.
11	Time of lab result	☺	Accurate and always captured.
12	Time of radiology order	☺	Accurate and always captured.
13	Time of radiology result	☺	Accurate and always captured.
14	Time of discharge order	☺	Not captured. Sometimes documented in the medical record.
15	Time of discharge assessment	☹	Not captured. Always documented in the medical record.
16	Time of discharge	☺	Captured but inaccurate. Discharge times are batch entered when things get quiet or at the end of a shift.

You also think you have the length of stay of nonurgent and minor patients, but do you? (See Exhibit 1.11.)

- You don't capture true time of arrival (#1) so there's a built-in error. The size of the error depends on how long patients wait in line to check in during busy hours.

- You capture triage category (#5), but it's not accurate—partially because of a clerical issue, and partially because the triage nurses inconsistently apply the scale.

- You capture discharge time (#16), but it's inaccurate.

You could try to improve based on time from registration (#2) to discharge (#16) for nonurgent and minor patients (#5), but you would be doomed to fail because the data is inaccurate.

Instead, you choose to first improve the data by validating and improving the accuracy of nurse triage (#5) and instituting a QC process for time of discharge (#16). You decide to ignore the built-in error because you don't capture true time of arrival (#1).

By first deciding what you will improve and how it will be measured, you have narrowed the QC process to one data element instead of 15. The other improvement—improving the accuracy of triage—will help all other clinical processes.

Exhibit 1.11

#	Data element	☺☺☹	Status
2	Time of registration	☺	**Accurate and always captured**
5	Triage category	☺	Captured but not accurate. **Actions: 1. Validation and training by staff educator on triage accuracy. 2. Routine audits of accuracy.**
16	Time of discharge	☺	Captured but inaccurate. Discharge times are batch entered when things get quiet or at the end of a shift. **Actions: 1. QC process implemented. 2. Periodic audits of accuracy.**

➔ Smoothing

We spoke of smoothing principles in the Introduction. These principles, to summarize the concept espoused by Litvak, are as follows:

- Variation is the enemy of efficient hospital operations
- Some types of variation are unavoidable: variation in physician qualifications, variation in clinical need, and variation in patient volumes
- Some types of variation are avoidable but common

We will talk about two important types of variation that are common but completely avoidable: variations in staffing of ancillary services, and variations in the scheduling of elective surgeries.

Smoothing of support services

The general public believes hospitals are fully functional 24 hours a day, seven days a
with hospitals knows most essentially shut down over the weekend. Try, for example, to ge
routine therapies or tests on a Saturday or Sunday:

- Dietary consults
- Physical therapy treatments or initial assessments
- Occupational therapy treatments or initial assessments
- Routine treadmill testing
- Routine magnetic resonance imaging or computed axial tomography scan
- Swallowing studies
- Routine echocardiograms (ECG)
- Routine nuclear medicine imaging
- Routine ultrasounds
- Case management/discharge planning

At many hospitals, if it isn't STAT, it's not being done on weekends.

Therefore, folks who come in on Friday will have to wait until Monday for important parts of their work-up
or treatment (Exhibit 1.12). This tradition in American health care robs the industry of two-sevenths
(almost 30%) of its functional capacity, and adds significant expenses for staffing the patient's "weekend
hotel" stay.

We are not saying that critical patients will not be taken care of. However, rarely is anyone discharged
directly from critical care. They first go the medical/surgical beds, often through a step-down unit. So if
Uncle Charlie has a medical problem on Wednesday, placed in critical care on Thursday (after a stint of
boarding in the ED), and improves on Friday, he is transferred to a medical surgical unit where he waits
until Monday to get ready for the discharge home.

Another example is a low-risk cardiac patient. Clinical practice guidelines indicate that it is safe to discharge
the patient as long as he or she has a treadmill ECG within 72 hours. However, due to back-ups in outpatient cardiology, the patient is kept in the hospital over the weekend, until the inpatient treadmill becomes
available for non-STAT testing.

How can one smooth this very unsmooth, complex process? A number of approaches have been successful. Some are expensive in terms of dollars and some are expensive in terms of physician buy-in, but all are
worth every dime.

Make your hospital a seven-day-per-week operation:

- Arrange for full therapist and technician coverage over the weekend. This can be done under contract, with per diem or agency personnel, or by staggering the shifts of full-time employees.

- Some integrated delivery systems have been able to implement a hospitalist specialty, where the attending physician can hand off a patient to a rounding team for inpatient care. It may be possible to extend this model to the weekend by working with larger hospitalizing physician groups and health plans. A weekend hospitalist team can take report from the attending on Friday, develop a care plan for the weekend, and contact the attending to discharge the patient. This is not a large problem for integrated systems such as university hospitals, the Veterans Administration, military hospitals, and large institutions like Kaiser. Many of these systems have a group of physicians who are mutually compensated and are at mutual risk. Establishing a weekend rounding team in those settings is a piece of cake (relatively speaking). But who pays in the private sector? There are ways, but they are not necessarily easy.

- Take your top diagnosis-related groups (DRGs) and reestablish care paths. One can then plan for weekend therapies and keep the attending informed of the patient's progress by telephone.

- Measure and hold accountable: The following metrics will be informative:

  - Length of stay of patients for the same DRG by day of week admitted
  - Response time for assessments and interventions by day of week

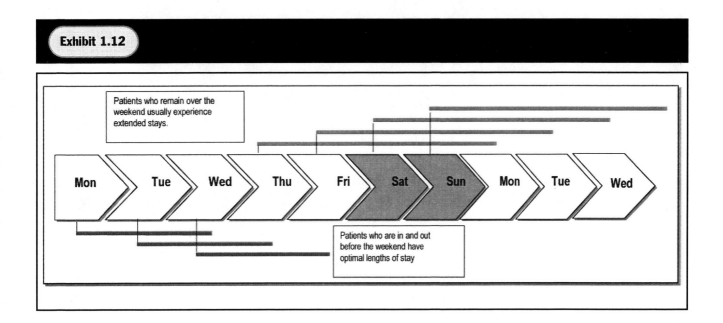

Exhibit 1.12

Patients who remain over the weekend usually experience extended stays.

Mon | Tue | Wed | Thu | Fri | Sat | Sun | Mon | Tue | Wed

Patients who are in and out before the weekend have optimal lengths of stay

Although we will discuss inpatient throughput in Subprocess 5, this approach—making the hospital a seven-day-a-week institution—is the single most important way to increase functional capacity. As you can see in Exhibit 1.12, "staffing down" on weekends has a profound impact on most patients.

As ancillary services experience weekend smoothing, there will be more beds available for the busiest days for the ED: Monday and Sunday.

Another interesting note: Studies have shown that patients who remain in the hospital over the weekend are much more likely to experience complications than those who are not there on the weekend. Why? Because hospital staffing is not smooth.

Smoothing elective surgeries

CONSIDER THIS WHEN:

Always.

Smoothing elective surgeries is a complex process. As Litvak explains, the scheduling of elective surgeries is complicated by the habits and office hours of many independent surgeons.

However, here are some approaches proven effective in smoothing elective surgeries:

- Have the same number of elective surgeries every day (at least Monday through Friday, that is—it will be a while until U.S. hospitals are ready for a full Saturday and Sunday).
- The mythical hospital in Exhibit 1.13 has six operating rooms (ORs) that are not used efficiently. By spreading the cases out during the day, the ORs are more efficient with savings in staff time.

Exhibit 1.13

OR Schedule Before Smoothing

	7 - 9	9 - 11	11 - 13	13 - 15	15 - 17
OR 1					
OR 2					
OR 3					
OR 4					
OR 5					
OR 6					

Same Day Admission   Outpatient   No Surgery

OR Schedule After Smoothing

	7 - 9	9 - 11	11 - 13	13 - 15	15 - 17
OR 1					
OR 2					
OR 3					
OR 4					
OR 5					
OR 6					

- The scheduling of same-day admissions should be optimized to not compete with the ED for hospital beds. In this idealized example (Exhibit 1.13), all of the same day admissions were moved to the front of the daily schedule.

- A predictable, smooth flow of admissions from surgery can be better accommodated by the bed Czar (see Subprocess 4) than can sporadic admissions during the day.

- As a corollary to this smoothing, physicians should make patient rounds early to identify potential discharges (to make room for their same-day admissions).

 # ED information management systems

CONSIDER THIS WHEN:

- The hospital already has good patient care processes.
- The ED is using a manual "white board" or other tracking tools effectively
- There is effective data-centric leadership.

Computerized tracking systems will only complicate flawed systems. However, they can help improve good processes.

When computerizing an ED works and when it doesn't

The first solution that often comes to mind for ED physician and nursing leaders is an automated information system.

And sure enough, sometimes a hospital installs a computer tracking system and things improve. Unfortunately, things just as often stay the same or become worse. Why?

We believe that computerizing a good system will make things better. Computerizing a dysfunctional system will either have no effect (other than wasting a lot of time and money) or will make things worse.

Said another way (by a good friend and expert computer systems analyst), one cannot computerize a nonsystem.

Tips for success and pitfalls to avoid:

- Before purchasing or installing a computer system, develop and maintain a manual system that works. For example, automated tracking systems are, at their core, computerized white boards (see section on white boards in Subprocess 2: ED throughput). However, if staff are not efficiently using a white board before computerization, they are unlikely to use one after computerization.

- Remember that interfacing with a computer is a barrier. Staff will no longer be able to look up to see what's on the white board. They will have to go to the computer terminal (which may not always be available) to study flow and availability. The placement and form of the user interface is therefore crucial to the system's ultimate success. For example, a large screen with an electronic white board may be a valuable feature.

- If you hope to have the computer automatically spew meaningful process data that need no further analysis, you're deluding yourself. Plan for analytical resources (either from the vendor or from internal support systems) to make the reports right for your systems.

- It is rare that a computer system will stimulate better documentation than a manual system. If staff are not documenting on the manual system, they are unlikely to be accurate with an electronic system.

- Ensure that there is minimal or no duplicate data entry: "interface" the complementary computer systems (e.g., interface the order entry systems with the ED system).

Patient- and equipment-tracking systems

An electronic tracking system has a number of basic features. It will

- locate patients and equipment within the department
- track patients waiting for bed placement
- assist in finding a match between a waiting patient and an available bed
- flash pending orders
- calculate throughput and turnaround times

Some patient- and equipment-tracking systems are very slick. One can tag equipment and locate key items without additional data entry. But beware, you must ask the right questions:

- Will the tracking system link to the hospital's radiology system? Its pharmacy system? Its laboratory system? Etc.?

- If it will interface, how much will the programming cost? Remember, interfaces are usually (in our experience, always) far more expensive and time consuming than initial estimates portray.
- Will leadership support the ultimate cost of the interfaces? If it will support the cost of the system but not the interface, don't get the system.
- Sometimes managers think that the interfaces can be justified after the system is installed and everyone can see what a great success it is. That rarely happens because, without the interface, the system often fails to achieve many of its stated goals.
- Without key interfaces, staff will rush to enter orders but not have time to update the tracking system.

- How does the user access the system? If leadership will support wireless tablets or omnipresent work stations, no problem. If there are just a few stations for input and reading, beware.
- Who will analyze the wealth of process data that will come out of the system? If that is unclear, don't go forward until accountability and resources are evident. There is nothing more frustrating than having a robust electronic tracking system but not having the right resources in place to make use of the data.

Electronic medical records systems

Another form of information system is a medical records documentation system. There are a number of outstanding documentation systems that allow multiple views of the same clinical information.

One particularly slick system is built off of the ED "T System®." The physician documentation module of the electronic T System prompts the user to common elements of a work-up based on the complaint. For example, a chest pain work-up prompts the physician toward the elements of assessment that could quickly lead to thrombolytic therapy. The user interface hinges on circles (for positive findings) and slashes (for negative findings). With practice and a wireless tablet, a physician can quickly document the assessment of a patient and have it returned in dictation-like format.

But the same caveats pertain to electronic medical records that pertain to electronic tracking systems. To be efficient and worthwhile, they should

- interface with existing laboratory, radiology, pharmacy, and other systems
- have convenient opportunities for user interface
- have the external or internal support necessary to train users and extract clinical and process information

Hybrid systems

The ideal would be a system that does both medical records documentation and patient tracking. Such systems are lauded. We are not aware of any that have proven themselves, but technology is improving daily. We suggest that you see the technology in action unless you're ready for an uncertain development process.

Beware of vaporware

Vaporware is computer slang for software that is not yet and may never be ready for "prime time." There have been many examples of vaporware, great ideas with fancy interfaces for demonstration purposes that never become real.

The complexity of electronic information systems and the uniqueness of each potential computer interface makes the development of ED information systems risky. There are relatively few potential customers, and the resources needed to develop and maintain such complex systems make for many examples of products that never get off the ground.

In other words, think long and hard before becoming the first kid on the block with your chosen ED information system.

Departmental leadership structure

We have years of experience evaluating EDs with significant problems. Our assessment process involves prolonged conversations with the nursing manager about the way things are done: How are patients greeted? What are your busiest times? How accurate is your triage system? How are patients transported to imaging?

What the manager thinks is happening is often not what is actually happening. Put in another way, there are usually a number of ED processes happening simultaneously. They include the process

- in the manager's mind
- that happens during the day
- that happens at night

- that happens on weekends
- that happens when "Chris" is the charge nurse
- that happens for Dr. Smith's patients

If variation is the enemy of quality and efficiency, then these unplanned variations must certainly hamper successful ED practices. The only way we've found to control inappropriate/unplanned variation in ED practices is to have a nursing management structure that is intimately involved in ED operations at all times with all staff.

Remember that an ED visit is a mini-hospitalization. Patients are admitted, worked-up, treated, and discharged (often to the inpatient units), all within one to five hours. Most of this occurs on the evening shift. The busiest days for EDs are often on weekends and Mondays.

Unless your ED has low volumes or your hospital has very few beds, having the house nursing supervisor cover the ED for nights and weekends is simply not enough.

Are we recommending a nurse manager in constant presence around the clock? Not necessarily. It is an unusual ED that truly needs such a rich ED management structure. However, hospitals should have a management structure for the ED that supports and supervises staff on all days of the week and during all shifts.

Supporting nursing practice

One reason management must be available is to improve and ensure nursing competency. For an ED team to function efficiently, nursing must (among other things)

- accurately assign triage categories
- anticipate the patient's and the physician's needs
- consistently implement approved protocols
- give accurate and appropriate discharge instructions
- be effective in facilitating inpatient admissions
- ensure consistent implementation of departmental policies

A nurse's skills must cover the spectrum of clinical populations and presentations, including

- pediatrics
- women in labor
- major trauma
- burns

- psychiatric disorders
- assaultive behavior
- acute bleeds
- shock
- myocardial infarction

The Emergency Nurses Association has catalogued most of the core skills necessary to be an efficient and effective nurse in its comprehensive *Core Curriculum*.

It is essential that staff have individual feedback on their performance in all of these areas. This feedback must come from someone who speaks for management.

The challenge of practice dissemination: Reducing variation

In addition to nursing practice, management must ensure that processes such as nursing protocols, admissions, and triage are implemented consistently. Why is this so difficult?

- ED processes are normally designed by teams that work days, even though the processes also affect the folks who work on evenings and nights
- New nurses are often assigned to nights and weekends (after orientation)
- Other hospital departments and community resources usually have different/diminished processes on nights and weekends

Somehow, all of these factors have to be known to management so that processes can be designed to account for these variable environments.

Examples of successful structures

There is no one management structure that is right for every institution, and each institution may have a number of options for providing coverage.

Management staffing must also be matched to the design of the ED (number of beds, number of modules or areas, the physical location of observation, etc.), nursing skill mix and staffing model, and whether charge nurses have a patient load or can dedicate themselves to matters such as patient flow and crisis management.

Full management coverage

Some busy or complex EDs (80,000 or so annual visits, multiple treatment areas) may choose a full-coverage model. This model appreciates that the manager is usually there during the day and is busy meeting with other departments, developing or improving processes, etc., and does not have time for the day-to-day functions described above. This "Full Management Coverage" model provides for a full-time clinical educator and QC personnel. Sometimes QC is done effectively through a "nursing peer review" mechanism, in which charts are reviewed as a group using pre-established criteria. The clinical educator usually conducts the session as a teaching opportunity. It tends to work very well.

In Exhibit 1.14, there are two assistant managers. Some hospitals have up to six. The manager and assistants adjust the schedule to make sure all days and all shifts are covered.

Exhibit 1.14

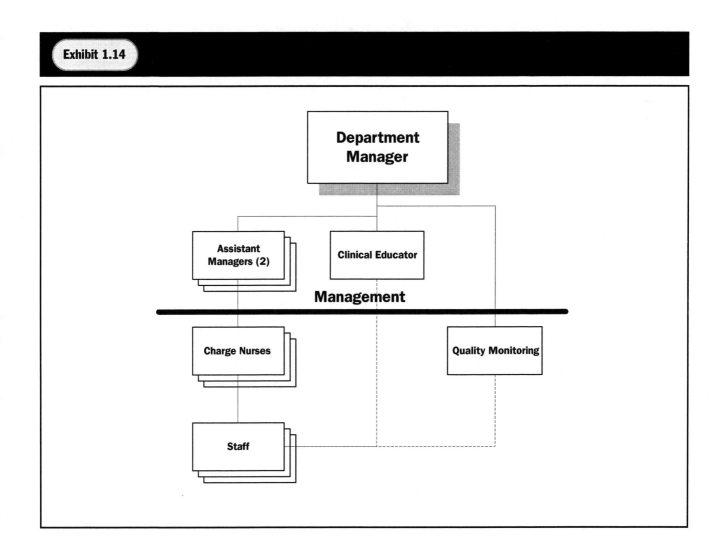

JCAHO's National Patient Safety Goals in the ED

Patient safety, including the new JCAHO National Patient Safety Goals, apply to the ED as well as the inpatient tower. Here is a reminder of what's required and some tips for implementation. Please be careful not to confuse our tips with the actual JCAHO requirement. Although we've printed the version of the JCAHO National Patient Safety Goals publicly available at the time this book went to press, the goals and requirements may change. Information about current standards and requirements is best obtained directly from the JCAHO at *www.jcaho.org*. Its frequently asked questions (FAQs) are updated often and carry the weight of the actual standards. Our intent here is to make the safety goals practical for the ED setting.

> **Goal 1a: Use of two patient identifiers for blood samples and medication administration.**

- Note that the second identifier is required for blood (lab) specimens AND medication administration.
- At the time of registration, ensure the proper identity of the patient by using a driver's license or other identification card. This does not complete the identification process, but it will help the institution find other medical records and accurately communicate with the patient.
- Assign a patient identification number to all patients at the time of registration. This number will then be printed on all medical records, including order sheets, medication administration records, nursing and physician notes, laboratory slips, labels, etc.
- Place an armband on all patients at the time of bed placement or triage, including ambulatory patients. (Although this is not required by the JCAHO for ambulatory patients, we highly recommend the practice.) The armband should contain name and identification number.
- DO NOT require documentation of the second identifier. It adds nothing to actual practice.
- DO reinforce patient identification practices often and with visual checklists.
- DO conduct observational studies of actual practices and improve performance as necessary based on the results.
- Combine monitoring for this goal with monitoring for other important safety and ED process elements (e.g., hand hygiene, restraint, pain management, protocol implementation, alarms, etc.).
- DO NOT lose credibility by asking nurses to repeat the patient's name once they know it. Ask them to check the patient identification number against the armband for blood draws and medications, but knowing the patient's face counts as one identifier.
- Have a formal rebanding procedure in place for missing or illegible wrist or ankle bands.

Goal 1b: Prior to the start of any surgical or invasive procedure, conduct a final verification process, such as a time out, to confirm the correct patient, procedure, and site. Do so using active—not passive—communication techniques.

- Use the "time out" whenever moderate or deep sedation is involved.
- Use standard forms or stamps to document high-risk procedures. Make sure the stamp or form has a place to document the time out.
- Encourage active communication for all ED interventions, such as during handoffs from one nurse or provider to another, or handoffs to ancillary departments for testing of critical patients.
- Monitor performance by observing actual practice, not just by looking at documentation.

Goal 2a: Implement a process for taking verbal or telephone orders, or critical test results that require a verification read-back of the complete order or test result by the person receiving the order or test result.

- DO NOT attempt to document the read-back in the medical record.
- DO monitor read-back of verbal orders through observational studies.
- Remind staff to write the order first then read-back what they have written.
- Instruct staff to be specific on number and concentrations, just like airplane pilots. For example, have them say "one-five" instead of "fifteen" and "five-oh" instead of "fifty."

Goal 2b: Standardize the abbreviations, acronyms, and symbols used throughout the organization, including a list of abbreviations, acronyms, and symbols not to use.

- Focus on abbreviations, acronyms, and symbols NOT TO USE. Standardizing abbreviations in general is a never-ending quest.
- Focus on the same DO NOT USE list as the main hospital. Consistency is essential.
- DO NOT overkill the number items of DO NOT USE list. Changing a few habits (such as Morphine Sulfate instead of MS) will be difficult. Changing a lot of habits at the same time will be impossible.
- Stay tuned to the JCAHO. They are likely to continue developing their own list of DO NOT USE abbreviations.

Goal 3a: Remove concentrated electrolytes (including, but not limited to, potassium chloride, potassium phosphate, and sodium chloride >0.9%) from patient care units.

- Concentrated electrolytes (e.g., 3% sodium chloride solution) should be dispensed with patient labels from pharmacy.
- The actual standard (MM.2.20 EP9) allows exceptions for when patient safety is at risk.
  - If certain electrolytes must be kept in floor stock in the ED, treat them as controlled substances (i.e., use a narcotics control record).

Goal 3b: Standardize and limit the number of drug concentrations available in the organization.

Goal 4a: Create and use a preoperative verification process, such as a checklist, to confirm that appropriate documents (e.g., medical records, imaging studies) are available.

- This goal applies to surgery, but see what you can do in the ED.
- Develop a moderate and deep sedation form that includes the checklist for high-risk procedures.

Goal 4d: Implement a process to mark the surgical site and involve the patient in the marking process.

- DO NOT site mark closed fracture reductions.
- DO NOT site mark nonlateralized procedures.

Goal 6b: Ensure that alarms are activated with appropriate settings and are sufficiently audible with respect to distances and competing noise within the unit.

Goal 7a: Comply with current Centers for Disease Control and Prevention (CDC) hand-hygiene guidelines.

- Current CDC hand-hygiene guidelines can be found in Appendix B at the end of this book.
- Place alcohol-based hand rubs at any bedside where there is not a handwash sink.
- CDC recommends 15-second handwashing. Staff can time 15 seconds by singing "Happy Birthday to You" slowly.
- Physicians must be trained along with nursing to wash hands.
- The CDC guidelines read like a political treatise, so develop user-friendly prompts and reminders.
- Perform observational studies and aggregate/trend data.
    - DO make the formal observational studies discipline-specific (nursing v. physician v. laboratory).
    - DO NOT make formal observational studies name-specific.
- Have charge nurses and managers give employee/physician-specific reinforcement.
- Believe it: Hand-hygiene makes a huge difference to clinical outcomes. ED staff may not see the results, but ICU staff usually do.

Human factors and patient safety

It may be an urban legend, but we understand that 50% of airplane crashes happen during a crew's first flight together.

Legend or not, the fact remains that the realities of health care make for a chaotic and unsafe environment. A number of health care organizations and specialties have looked to the lessons learned in aviation safety to make the hospital workplace safe for patients and staff alike. Kaiser Permanente, for example, has made human factors a pivotal strategy in its industry-leading efforts to enhance patient safety. This book is not really about this type of approach, but we believe in the principle and encourage those seeking to improve operations to reflect on human factors as they attempt to develop new systems. There are a number of human factors approaches that apply to a health care setting. Here are a few:

- Develop checklists for high-risk procedures. (Would you want to fly on an airplane where the crew was not using a pre-flight checklist?)

- Work with leadership to develop a team culture rather than a "physician is team" culture. This must be led by the physicians. There is a growing number of champions for this approach, which puts the patient ahead of the egos.

- Develop and complete a team briefing prior to high-risk procedures. Although JCAHO requires a briefing to address site marking and patient identification, a more complete team briefing is being adopted by many organizations. The briefing is intended to promote complete communication. Each team member is expected to introduce him- or herself by name and role (when appropriate) and briefly review the patient's status and the intended course of the intervention. Literature suggests that outcomes improve when time is taken to communicate about roles, the procedure, and the patient.

- Encourage full communication:

    - Enable nursing staff with the expectation that they will question the physician or other caregivers when they are uncertain about an order or any other aspect of care.

    - Train staff on how and when to raise these questions.

    - Remind physicians to encourage silly questions (in the appropriate setting).

Will changing the culture of health care along these lines be quick and easy? No. Is it essential to improve the safety and efficiency of our ever-challenged health care system? Absolutely.

SUBPROCESS 1

ED INTAKE: *FROM PRESENTATION TO PROVIDER EXAMINATION*

Subprocess 1

ED INTAKE: FROM PRESENTATION TO PROVIDER EXAMINATION

Reception of ambulatory patients

 ### *Log*

The Emergency Medical Treatment and Active Labor Act (EMTALA) and common sense both dictate that all patients presenting to the Emergency Department (ED) be entered into a log. The log is a key data collection tool. The log should contain the following:

- Patient name
- Medical record number, driver's license number, other unambiguous form of identification (a unique patient identifier)
- Date and time of arrival or presentation (see time of arrival below)
- State law and other considerations usually drive the collection of a number of other data elements (e.g. complaint, disposition, etc.)

 ### *Collecting time of arrival*

CONSIDER THIS WHEN:

- Time to provider is an issue
- Patients sometimes wait more than 10 minutes to initiation of triage
- LWBS rates are greater than 4%

In an ideal world, the patient's true time of arrival would be collected in the log. This time could then be used to accurately measure time to triage and bed placement.

However, many EDs choose not to collect true time of arrival. The time of arrival listed on the ED log is actually the time the patient was interviewed by a receptionist or triage nurse.

Collecting time of interview/interaction is not a problem if there are never significant waits for this interaction. However, many departments have times during the day when the incoming patient flow exceeds the capacity of the intake process.

Take a close look at the scatter diagram below, Exhibit 2.1. It graphs the amount of time each patient waited before being seen by a physician, based on documentation in the medical record. The vertical (y) axis measures the length of time (hours and minutes) it took to see the doctor. The horizontal (x) axis indicates the time of day. Each patient in the sample was assigned a triage category based on a modified Canadian five-level triage scale: resuscitative (R), emergent (E), urgent (U), nonurgent (N) and minor (M).

You will note that wait times were not equal throughout the day, ballooning during the midday hours.

Exhibit 2.1

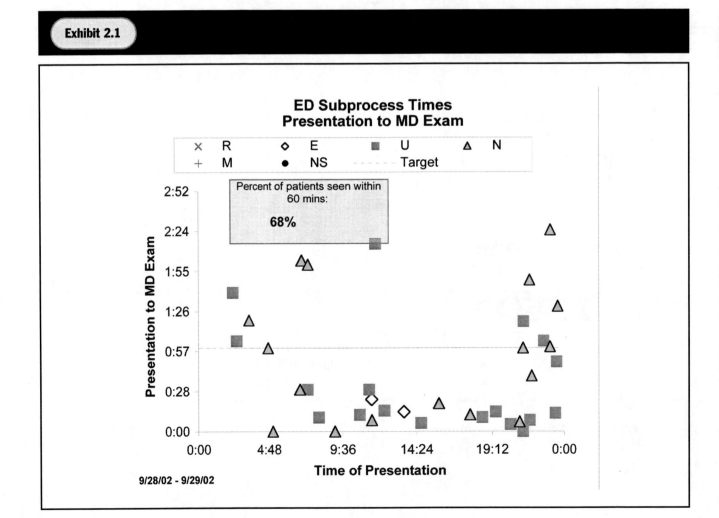

This data collection, however, was inaccurate due to the queuing paradox. That is, when there were long waits for physicians, there were also long waits for triage. Because true time of arrival was not collected, the true magnitude of the differences in wait times was muted. Had true time of arrival been documented, the amplitude of the variation in wait time would have revealed itself to be significantly greater. See Exhibit 2.2.

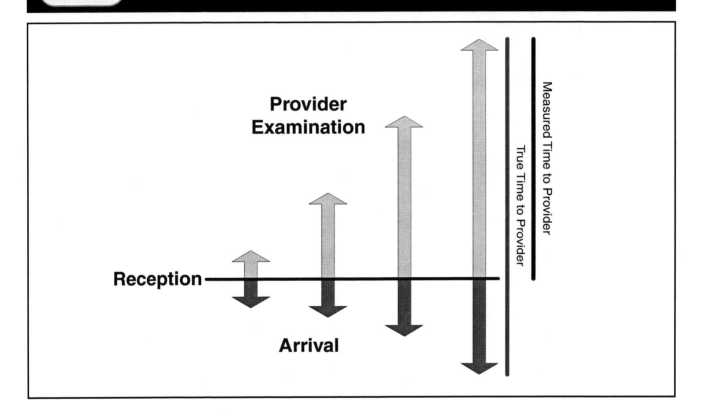

Approaches to collecting true time of arrival

Some medical centers have ambulatory patients complete a simple form as they walk through the door. Doing so helps the triage nurse keep track of the order of triage. By depositing the forms in a covered tray, the center preserves patient confidentiality. Take care with this approach, however. Some patients may miss their triage if they don't sign the form. It is necessary that the forms be evident and staff be vigilant in looking for confused patients.

Other medical centers have a volunteer or receptionist responsible for both collecting true time of arrival and completing an accurate log.

→ Nurse first

Some patients wait more than 10 minutes for triage

Some EDs make a receptionist or greeter be the first point of contact. We strongly encourage a "nurse first" model, in which the nurse initiates and, when practical, completes triage. The nurse then gives triage paperwork to the receptionist for registration (if there is a wait for bed placement) or registration as completed at the bedside.

Exhibit 2.3

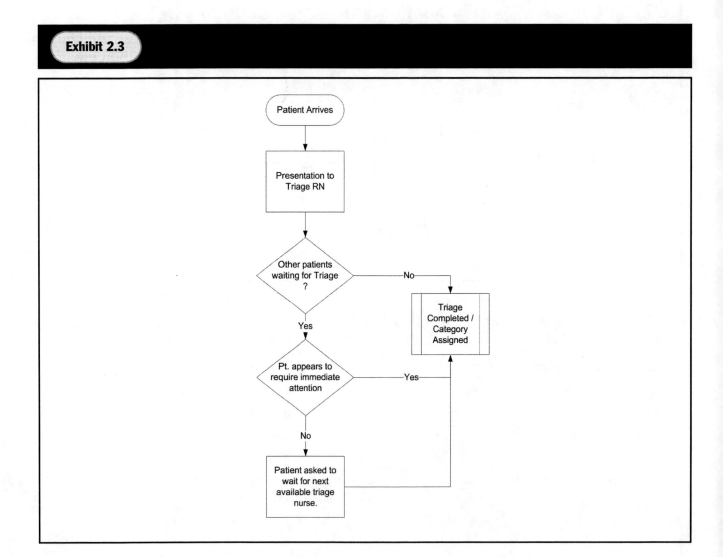

This approach has the following advantages:

1. **EMTALA vulnerabilities are reduced.** A high percentage of EMTALA violations relate to patients who wait for medical screening. For example, one hospital was cited because a patient, who later left and committed suicide, waited two hours before being seen by a nurse. Had the nurse done a 30-second assessment of the patient, the patient probably would have been seen, and the federal government would have less of an argument that medical screening (which begins at triage) had not been done. Many other examples of EMTALA violations relate to clerks advising patients about options for care before triage, or—much worse—discussing fees before the beginning of the clinical assessment.

2. **Serious illnesses are likely to be identified earlier in the process.** When volume is low, the triage nurse has plenty of time to complete triage. When the ED becomes busy, the triage nurse may take a long time to completely assess the patient, especially if the triage assessments take longer than the ideal two to five minutes per patient. Therefore, during busy times, it is safer for a registered nurse to quickly scan patients and hear their complaints before allowing them to wait for a full assessment.

3. **Some patients will be seen more quickly.** If the triage nurse knows of available beds (see below), he or she can take the patient to one immediately when it becomes available. Although triage is intended to allocate scarce resources, the patient should not have to wait for care when resources are abundant (i.e., beds and staff are available in the back).

4. **The patient is more likely to be satisfied and to not leave before having been seen.** The patient will know that a clinical person has evaluated his or her complaint. If the patient sees a clerk—who can do little to address the complaint—he or she is more likely to become agitated.

5. **Triage interventions and protocols can be more quickly initiated.** The triage nurse can initiate an x-ray protocol, give the patient a cool pack to address a painful extremity, or administer medication to lower a fever even before a complete triage exam is performed.

6. **This approach works well with other best front-end practices.** In the nurse first model, the flexible one-step triage process may be implemented, team assignments may be expedited, and protocols may be made more effective.

Tips:

- When the nurse cannot complete triage in one step, initial patient reception by the registered nurse (RN) should be very brief. The RN should merely judge that the patient is all right to wait, and should not assign a triage category.
- Measure the process time to triage from the time of true arrival (optimally) or time of nurse reception (plan "B") to the time of triage end.
- If a child arrives and complains of fever, take a tympanic temperature before having the patient wait for the completion of triage.
- If an adult complains of high blood pressure, check it quickly before offering him or her a seat.

→ # Triage reassessments

Each hospital should have a policy that guides staff about when to do a brief nursing check (rather than a true reassessment) of waiting patients.

> **CONSIDER THIS WHEN:**
> - Some patients wait more than 30 minutes for a physician examination
> - You use a reliable five-tier triage system

- Some hospitals do not address this issue at all, leaving it to the judgment of the nurse. We do not recommend this unless time to bed placement is not a problem.
- Other hospitals establish a flat "reassessment" time frame. Nurses rarely adhere to such time frames for reasons discussed below.
- We prefer "rechecks" of waiting patients based on triage acuity score.

The Canadian Triage System[1] establishes maximum expected wait times by triage category. These times are called operational objectives rather than standards of care, an important distinction, since regulators and courts are unforgiving when a hospital fails to meet its own standard of care. They were arrived at by professional consensus in Canada. Operational objectives for time to provider are

- emergent: 15 minutes
- urgent: 30 minutes
- nonurgent: 60 minutes
- minor: 120 minutes

---

[1] The Canadian Triage and Acuity Scale (CTAS) for Emergency Departments, Berveridge, R. Versim, 16, 11/14/98, www.caep.ca.

A hospital could select these objectives or establish different ones, as long as medical staff agree that the target wait times are clinically appropriate. Rechecks should be performed for patients waiting longer than the operational objectives dictate.

Tips:

- Adopt a recheck policy if there are times of significant waits for care.

- Do not fall into the reassessment trap. If things are busy in the back, thus delaying bed placement, things are usually busy in the front as well. Therefore, triage nurses will be hard pressed to do more than a recheck.

- If the hospital does not have a computer tracking system that can flag wait times by triage acuity, develop a triage "rack" system (see below) to visually track rechecks.

- Make sure the triage form includes a quick and convenient space to record the rechecks.

- Make it clear that rechecks do not necessarily mean a hands-on assessment of the patient. Sometimes a quick visualization or verbal comment is enough to determine that his or her condition has not significantly deteriorated.

- Technicians (licensed vocational nurse [LVN]/licensed practical nurse [LPN]/emergency medical technician [EMT]) can assist the triage RN in performing rechecks.

The goal is not to perform a lot of rechecks. The goal is to meet operational objectives for provider examinations. Holding the triage nurse accountable for rechecks establishes a natural "push" to bed placement. It also establishes a degree of safety for waiting patients.

→ *Triage rack systems*

CONSIDER THIS WHEN:
- Some patients wait more than 30 minutes for a physician examination
- The hospital does not have reliable patient wait information on a computerized tracking system
- The ED uses a reliable five-tier triage scale

There are many successful triage rack systems. The model that works for your triage area will be best designed by the triage nurses and technicians who use it. We offer one idea as a thought stimulator.

Rack by triage acuity

Have a different slot for each triage acuity. Order the triage slips in the rack by time of arrival. (See Exhibit 2.4) This system has the following advantages:

- It is easy
- It will help trigger a virtual fast track operation
- It helps the charge nurse or triage team leader monitor the number of urgent patients

Exhibit 2.4

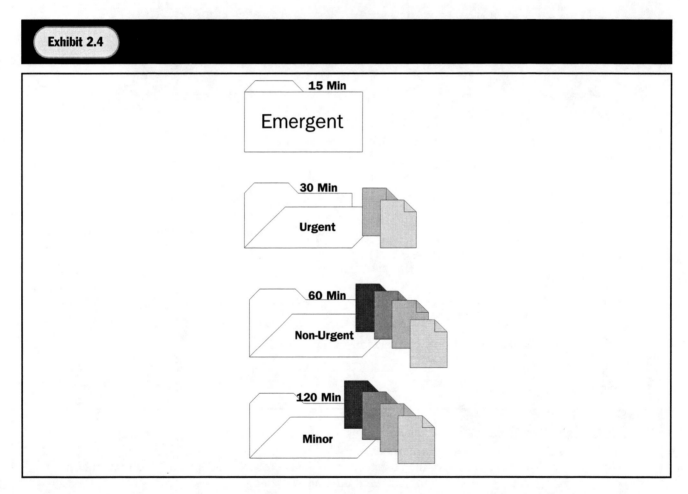

Beware: If the ED is busy, it's easy to let minor and nonurgent patients linger. Consider a trigger for virtual fast track instead. It will clear out the waiting room, increase customer satisfaction, decrease the number of LWBSs, and increase collectibles.

Technician support for triage

CONSIDER THIS WHEN:

There are predictable times when the waiting room will be crowded with waiting patients

---

Many successful EDs have made efficient use of technicians and LVNs.

A technician can be helpful in the triage area, especially in communicating with patients. Technicians are helpful in facilitating rechecks, taking temperatures and blood pressures, giving ice packs, and responding to the inquiries of waiting patients.

Triage accuracy and consistency

Many ED managers will say good triage nurses can manage the order of care with little or no assistance. Based on their experience, they know who needs to be seen next.

Unfortunately, however, not all triage nurses have equal skill levels, and ED intake processes vary wildly without a reliable system.

Why is objective, reliable triage important?

If your ED never has waits for physician examinations, please skip to the next section . . . in fact, please return this book and get your money back.

However, if your institution is like just about every hospital in the nation, there are times when patients have to wait. For those institutions, objective, reliable triage is very important.

- **For quality reasons.** No institution wants to have unstable patients or patients with life-threatening conditions wait for care. It is therefore traditional and essential that someone with assessment capabilities examine patients to determine the order of care. This person—usually an RN—must quickly and accurately identify chest pain patients who are candidates for thrombolytic therapy, patients with signs of shock, patients who could have a health crisis, etc. An accurate, repeatable triage system is the only way to ensure consistent identification of patients in distress.

- **For data reasons.** EDs and hospitals must track performance to ensure quality and efficiency. Without a reliable triage system, performance is hard to measure. Taking a long time to care for patients with minor injuries is one issue. Taking a long time to see patients with a potentially severe illness is quite different.

- **For efficiency reasons.** Without a reliable triage system, it is impossible to implement practices to help the ED run smoothly, such as triggers for fast track, triggers for immediate bed placement, initiation of triage protocols, etc.

Triage at the back door, too

Many institutions believe that patients who come in by ambulance require immediate bed placement. However, some ambulance patients have only minor injuries, and may take a bed that could be used better to assess and treat a patient in the waiting room.

Therefore, we recommend that triage categories be assigned to ambulance patients by patient care nurses in the back. The charge nurse, in coordination with the triage team leader, can then decide whether the patient is taken from the EMT gurney to the bed or from the gurney to the waiting room.

 ## Five-tier triage systems

CONSIDER THIS WHEN:
- Some patients wait more than 30 minutes for a physician examination
- Some patients wait more than 10 minutes for triage
- There are quality concerns over the triage process
- Reliable data on front-end processes is necessary

Most EDs in the United States use a three-tier triage scale, such as the model espoused by the Emergency Nurses Association in the 1990s. This three-tier system has not worked as well as we hoped.

The typical three-tier system assigns patients to emergent, urgent, and nonurgent categories. The problem is that the majority of patients end up in the urgent category, so the system does not help assign an order of care. Therefore, the Emergency Nurses Association and other experts in emergency care recommend a five-tier system instead.

Five-tier systems essentially break the urgent category in two. The fifth and most acute tier is reserved for resuscitations.

We will discuss three popular five-tier systems, and then make our personal recommendation.

Manchester

The Manchester (England) triage scale is a truly outstanding set of triage algorithms. It takes common complaints and runs them through a series of assessment findings to arrive at a triage category.

Advantages	Disadvantages
• Clinically complete • Elegant • Very useful for training	• Complex to implement for nurses, with multiple clinical conditions each with various indicators. • Sometimes crosses into physician assessment skill set.

Canadian

The national health care systems in Australia and Canada have each developed a common triage system to be used nationwide. The Canadian system has been more widely adopted and adapted in the United States than the Australian system.

The Canadian system establishes the following levels:

- Level I: resuscitation
- Level II: emergent
- Level III: urgent
- Level IV: less urgent
- Level V: nonurgent

The Canadian triage system and implementation guide provide an exhaustive list of complaints and findings to inform a triage nurse's decision. It is ready to implement straight from the Web site, complete with wall plaques and training material.

Advantages	Disadvantages
• Clinically complete • Developed through a national consensus in Canada • Ready to use "off the shelf" with implementation and education modules • Good for training new triage nurses	• The operational objectives of the Canadian system may not fit the hospital's imperatives. • The system has a lot of detail, with some conditions spanning a number of triage categories with only subtle differences among designations.

Emergency Severity Index

Wuerz, et al., developed the Emergency Severity Index (ESI)[2] Working at Massachusetts General and other hospitals, version two of the system (now published by the Emergency Nurses Association) has proven to have high inter-rater reliability and to be valid in terms of predicting the need for admission.

The algorithm uses general descriptors of the patient's condition, classifying patients into five levels:

- Level 1: unresponsive, intubated, etc.
- Level 2: confused and lethargic, severe pain, respiratory distress, unstable vital signs
- Level 3: multiple resources necessary (imaging, consultations, etc.)
- Level 4: one resource necessary
- Level 5: no resources necessary

The authors' pick

For an "off the shelf" system, we prefer the Canadian Triage System, although the ESI may also mature into an implementation-ready product. Our only reservation about the ESI is the designation of severe pain and its application by nurses who are new to triage (see "Pain and triage" on p. 53).

---

[2] Emergency Severity Index Implementation, Handbook, Gilboy, Nicki, et al. 2003. www.ena.org.

Advantages	Disadvantages
• Simple to use/elegant • Minimal teaching necessary to experienced triage nurses • Consistency among triage nurses • Predictive of need for admission • Resource leveling for lower categories is helpful for assignment of patient flow	• May not be comparable across hospitals because of differences in resource utilization. • Requires objective measures of severe pain. • May not be useful for nurses who are new to triage.

In a perfect world, one system would combine the elegance and simplicity of ESI with the national consensus of the Canadian system. We urge hospitals to carefully evaluate all of these five-tier systems before choosing one.

No matter which system you choose, however, you should definitely shift from three to five tiers.

Pain and triage

A patient with an injury to the left ankle is being assessed by the triage nurse. The nurse asks, "On a scale of 0 to 10, with 10 being the worst pain imaginable and 0 being no pain at all, how would you rate your ankle pain?" The patient responds that the pain is 10 out of 10, and then walks with a slight limp to the waiting room.

All published triage systems classify severe pain as requiring immediate examination. Unfortunately, severe pain is not well defined and, since most published pain scales rate the patient's subjective opinion, the ankle injury above would rate an "emergent" ranking. However, this is neither intended by triage scales nor appropriate to the situation.

The Canadian triage system gives some guidance about pain, and indicates that pain that can be abated in the waiting room does not, by itself, warrant upgrading to emergent.

Kaiser Permanente in Southern California recently developed an RN Assessed Pain Scale (RAPS)[3] This scale is used for triage purposes only and, when combined with the organization's adaptation of the

Canadian Triage and Acuity Scale, gives specific guidance as to which reports of pain should be considered emergent. Like the implementation guide in the Canadian triage system, RAPS also prompts the triage nurse to initiate interventions to lessen the waiting patient's pain.

→ **The two- to five-minute triage assessment**

CONCENTRATE ON THE LENGTH OF TRIAGE WHEN

- Triage nurses spend more than five minutes on <u>some</u> patients
- Triage nurses spend more than two minutes on <u>most</u> patients
- The entire triage turnaround process takes more than seven minutes

When a number of patients are waiting for triage or bed placement, it is neither necessary nor appropriate to perform a detailed nursing assessment. Semiurgent and nonurgent (Canadian terms for the lower two of five levels) patients may need only a physician or physician extender's work up—a full nursing assessment beyond triage may be unnecessary. Patients with higher acuity should be seen by the physician as soon as possible, and prolonging the nursing assessment at triage will only add to the delay. There is one important exception to this concept: If there are extensive waits for a bed in the back, the nurse may need to spend more time with higher acuity patients.

The goal of the triage assessment is to determine the order of care. Once the nurse has enough information to do this, he or she is done with triage. The Emergency Nurses Association believes that no triage assessment should take longer than five minutes. Some can be as brief as two.

If you find that triage assessments are taking too long at your medical center, consider the following:

- Examine the triage documentation form. It should be short and flow logically through the assessment process. Is it driving the collection of unnecessary information, or of data that will be repeated once the patient is placed in a bed?
- Study the triage process to identify and eliminate unnecessary delays.
- Deploy a triage nurse educator to work with triage nurses.

---

[3] *Kaiser Permanente is in the process of submitting RAPS for publication.*

MYTH BUSTER

Neither good medical practice nor JCAHO standards require a nursing assessment for ambulatory patients, even if they present to the ED. Instead, a medical screening examination is required by EMTALA. This can be performed by the physician, nurse practitioner, physician's assistant, or other professional as appropriate to the condition of the patient. We call this a provider-based care unit. As long as patients are seen in a timely manner (e.g., nonurgent patients within 60 minutes and minor patients seen within 120 minutes), a nursing assessment beyond triage is not indicated. However, nursing assessments will become vital should there be significant delays beyond the triage process.

MYTH BUSTER

Triage is not a required ED process. However, it is the beginning of EMTALA's medical screening process when prompt physician examinations cannot be assured to all presenting. Since there are few departments that can guarantee "immediate seating" in the back, a front-end triage process is traditional. Some have solved the immediate seating issue by moving a physician, physician assistant, or nurse practitioner up to the triage area.

MYTH BUSTER

JCAHO does not require the measurement of head circumference and length for all pediatric patients presenting to the ED (most infants are brought in due to fevers or unusual crying). JCAHO allows the hospital to define the scope of the ambulatory assessment, including children seen on an ambulatory basis. However, head circumference and length will be an important part of the work-up for admitted children or infants seen on an ambulatory basis for certain complaints.

- When it comes to these issues, follow rule #1 of compliance: Say what you do and do what you say.
- DO NOT slow down the triage process by including irrelevant assessment elements in the name of a mythical accreditation requirement.
- Remember: If it doesn't make clinical sense, it's really not required (even if you heard it during a survey).

Orthostatic vital signs

We find orthostatic vital signs to be notably underused and underappreciated by triage nurses. A 10% drop in blood pressure or a 10% increase in heart rate as a patient moves from sitting to standing or laying to sitting is a sign of potential hypovolemia.

- Orthostatic vial signs should not be taken for every triage.
- Orthostatic vital signs should be taken when indicated by the complaint (abdominal pain, bleeding, prolonged vomiting or diarrhea, etc.) or condition.
- When orthostatic changes are present, the triage category will usually change (at least to urgent under most triage systems).

 ### *Triage documentation tools*

CONSIDER THIS WHEN:

- Triage nurses spend more than five minutes on some patients
- Triage nurses spend more than two minutes on most patients
- The entire triage turnaround process (from the beginning of one triage to the beginning of the next) is more than seven minutes
- Physicians complain of not receiving enough information

Remember the following points in designing or redesigning a triage documentation tool:

- Involve triage nurses, the ED clinical educator, and quality monitoring staff in the design of the tool.
- Start with a tool most staff like, and modify or improve the tool to streamline documentation while collecting essential elements.
- Ask physicians which information is truly useful to them once the patient is in the back. Most will say they primarily use the presenting complaint and vital signs.
- Make sure pain documentation is complete:
  - The patient's subjective scale should always be reported
  - If an objective scale (like Kaiser Permanente's RAPS) is available, the components that led up to the total score should be indicated
  - Other relevant information should be present, such as quality, what provokes the pain, whether it radiates, etc.
  - Pain interventions such as ice or pillows should be offered and documented

- Provide fields for important process times:
    - Time of arrival
    - Time of triage start
    - Time of triage end/level assigned
    - Time of recheck while waiting
- Leave room for narrative documentation of subjective and objective information.

 ## Documenting LWBS patients

CONSIDER THIS WHEN:

- The LWBS rate is greater than 4%
- There are concerns about compliance vulnerabilities
- Patient's satisfaction scores are low

There are a number of reasons to document when and in what condition a patient leaves without being seen. One of them is that it's required by the EMTALA interpretive guidelines.

Here's one way to catch the information:

- Have a standard location to document LWBS cases. Some use a separate form, but most use an existing documentation tool.
- If staff are unaware the patient has left:
    - Call for the patient three times, approximately 15 minutes apart
    - Document the times of each call
    - Classify the patient as LWBS if the patient does not answer on the third call
    - Log that the patient LWBS at the time of the first call
- If staff are aware that the patient is leaving:
    - Encourage the patient to stay
    - Be realistic about the expected wait for a provider examination
    - Document the discussion in a consistent location within the medical record
    - Document how the patient appears, even if a nonclinical person is having the interaction
    - Consider instituting quality control checks of random charts before they are sent to medical records

┌───┐

DRIVER'S LICENSE OR ID CARD PLEASE

Some institutions increase interactions between patients and staff when the patient leaves without being seen by collecting the patient's driver's license or other identification card at the time of triage. Although there are pitfalls to this approach, some have been successful with it. Those who use it successfully have decreased their LWBS rate and increased satisfaction through increased interaction with trained and scripted staff.

└───┘

Check box v. narrative

The best triage documentation we've ever seen used a blank half-sheet form with demographics, complaints, and vital signs at the top. The rest was narrative. Some of the worst triage documentation we've ever seen was on a detailed triage form with many prompts for the various assessment elements.

Does this mean that prompts are bad? No—it simply means that prompts alone have limited value. Whatever documentation tool the hospital uses, it must be accompanied by meaningful review (e.g., audits for completeness) and feedback to staff.

Complaint-driven triage documentation tools

Some EDs have adopted complaint-specific templates in an attempt to improve triage accuracy and documentation. As discussed above, the department's success is directly proportional to the amount of management/educational involvement, rather than to the elegance of the form.

That said, some hospitals have been successful in developing triage tools specific to chest pain, abdominal pain, behavioral problems, pediatric complaints, gynecological complaints, etc.

Triage out

Some medical centers would like to route patients with minor illnesses to other settings, due to capacity concerns in the main ED. This is where EMTALA begins to play a significant role in ED operations.

MYTH BUSTER

Many believe that EMTALA requires that patients who present to the ED be seen in the ED. Yes, the hospital must medically screen and stabilize the patient, but patients who present to the ED may be seen in another clinically appropriate location within the hospital.

- EMTALA requires that all patients who present to the ED for any medical condition receive a medical screening examination and necessary stabilizing care within the hospital.

- EMTALA does not require that all patients be seen in the ED. For example, patients with minor complaints may be triaged to a hospital clinic on the campus, and patients in labor may be triaged to labor and delivery.

Some institutions have attempted to triage patients to nonhospital locations, such as nearby nonhospital medical offices. In doing so, they claim that the triage process constitutes a medical screening since it classified the patient in a minor or nonurgent triage category.

We do not recommend this practice for the following reasons:

- A triage assessment is intended to establish an order of care, not to substitute for a medical screening examination.

- Although some believe that a triage nurse is qualified to rule out an emergency medical condition for minor complaints, the standard of documentation required for medical screening is greater than that required for triage.

- Nurses who are responsible for medical screening (as opposed to triage) tend to take far longer than the recommended two to five minutes for the triage assessment, sometimes taking up to 30 minutes. They thereby delay downstream triage activities and exacerbate rather than relieve waits for care.

- Triage nurse medical screening must be guided by extensive protocols to satisfy regulators. No matter how complex, such protocols are notoriously incomplete. Yet, the more complex the protocol, the more difficult it is to follow.

- We've observed that physicians tend to pressure nurses to "triage out" patients who don't meet the elements of the protocol.

In summary, it is often useful and appropriate to triage patients to other parts of the hospital. However, such patients should be triaged to nearby, easy-to-find venues (normally in the same building, always on the same campus) that are part of the hospital (covered by the hospital's Medicare provider number).

Bracelets and ID cards

CONSIDER THIS WHEN:

Always

There are two different types of identification that are very important when the patient enters the ED:

- Finding out who the patient actually is (to ensure past clinical information the hospital may have on the patient is properly attributed, to prevent Medicare or insurance fraud, etc.)

- Once you know their unique identity, making sure that caregivers will not confuse the patient with other patients

Identifying the patient

At some point during the triage and registration process, it will be appropriate to ask for the patient's identification. Each front-end set up is different, and some patients arrive through the back door, so the exact flow will vary.

- When possible, ask to see the patient's identity cards (including driver's license, passport, or any photo identification)

- Read back the identification information, include the spelling of the name, the date of birth, and any other element that will be important in downstream identification

- Prepare a patient ID bracelet and follow your process for affixing the bracelet to the patient

Distinct identification bracelets

We prefer bright identification bracelets that are unique to the ED (e.g., fluorescent orange or green) to distinctly identify the patient as an ED patient. That way, the imaging department or laboratory can tell from across the room that the patient was referred from the ED. Efforts are then made to meet their performance standards.

We recommend that all patients be banded at the time of registration. In that way, waiting patients can be distinguished from family members. It will also facilitate across-the-room rechecks for waiting patients. This may take a little patient education ("We're going to put this on you right now so we can serve you better. We'll need to double check in case we have to do laboratory testing or give you any medications.") ID bracelets do not raise HIPAA or other confidentiality concerns.

The tag inside the bracelet should comply with hospital policy and have the same patient identifiers used everywhere else in the facility to ensure safe patient care. These identifiers typically include the patient's name, medical record number, and date of birth, etc.

EMTALA CAUTION:

If the patient offers insurance information at the time of registration, accept it. However, be careful not to inadvertently accrue EMTALA troubles by delaying triage or medical screening to check on the patient's insurance status or ability to pay.

Normally, asking for the patient's insurance card during registration does not delay care and is acceptable. However, be aware of the following:

- Some states, such as California, have made it illegal to even inquire about ability to pay prior to medical screening.

- A deposit may not be requested before the physician sees (and, if necessary, stabilizes) the patient.

- The patient may ask "how much will this cost?" Of course, you won't know the total fee at the time of registration. However, the patient has a right to some sort of response (e.g., a fee schedule, normal charges, etc.). In other words, discussing finances with the patient is appropriate if he or she asks.

- If patients decide to leave during the registration process, be sure to inform them again of their right to a medical screening examination and document the interaction (who said what, etc.).

JCAHO SURVEY TIP

If a surveyor ever asks how you identify the patient when giving medications or drawing blood

- do not say, "I check the arm band," even though that's the process
- instead say, "I check the patient's name and medical record number/date of birth against the (medication order sheet/mediation administration record/lab slip)"

→ Triage team leader

CONSIDER THIS WHEN:

- Time from arrival to triage start is sometimes more than 10 minutes
- More than one triage nurse is necessary to handle patient volume

The primary function of the triage nurse is to assess patients one at a time to determine the order of care. However, triage nurses are also accountable for rechecking waiting patients, deciding when to go from a one-step to a two-step triage process, triggering fast tracking of minor patients, triggering a backup mechanism, etc. When only one triage nurse is assigned, that accountability is clear. When two or more triage nurses are brought to the front, however, one nurse should be the triage team leader. Prepare a formal duty list for the triage team leader. In addition to triaging patients, the triage team leader should be accountable for

- communication with the charge nurse
- triggering the triage backup plan
- triggering the two-step triage system
- triggering fast track
- directing technicians who may be assigned to assist the triage nurses
- ensuring that waiting patients can continue to safely wait for care
- working the triage chart rack
- ensuring rechecks for waiting patients

→ ## Bypassing the waiting room

CONSIDER THIS WHEN:

- There are times of the day when there are available beds/providers within the ED
- There is good communication between triage and the main ED
- The triage nurse has autonomy for bed placement

A wise friend of ours, who is the medical director of a very busy and undersized ED, continually reminds us that triage is intended to determine the order of care when resources for immediate care are not available. However, our front-end systems are typically set up in a linear fashion. Patients tend to get triaged when beds are immediately available. For some hospitals, it takes about 30 minutes for a patient to sign in, get a triage assessment, register be placed in a bed, and wait for a physician's examination if there is no backup.

One hospital we know is designing a new ED without a main waiting room to try to break down this linear thinking. Patients will be taken directly to one of the four treatment modules. If there is a wait for bed placement, it will be in a waiting room within the treatment module. The goal is to have parallel processes to expedite care. A bottleneck may occur at any resource: There can be a wait for triage, registration, a bed, the bedside nurse, or the physician. Any of these waits will delay care. This innovative (but as yet untested) design is intended to take advantage of any possible shortcut to a physician's examination. In the ED, remember, timeliness is quality. There are also two common operational approaches to trying to break down this bottleneck:

Approach 1: The faster bed track

For this approach, the triage nurse must have autonomy for bed placement and knowledge of available beds in the ED. It's also helpful to have an "open ED design," where a bed is a bed is a bed (critical patients not withstanding). (See Exhibit 2.5.) If a bed is available in the back, the nurse takes the complaint and vital signs, enters a quick registration, and takes the patient directly to a bed. The patient care nurse at the bedside completes the initial assessment.

Approach 2: Triage and register at the bedside

In this approach, the patient is ushered directly into the open ED bed, where presenting complaint and other elements of reception and registration are performed.

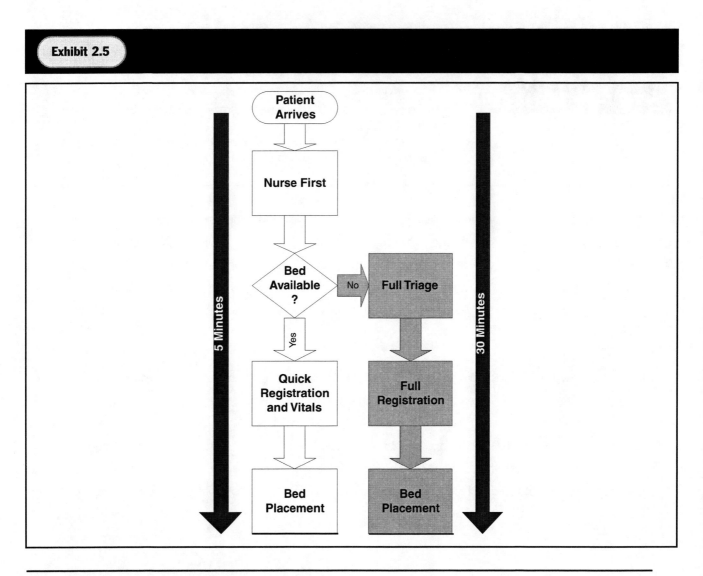

Exhibit 2.5

Flexible one-step triage systems

CONSIDER THIS WHEN:

- There are times during the day when triage backs up
- Triage is normally efficient, lasting only two to five minutes

When there are enough triage nurses to meet demand, the nurse can greet the patient and perform a triage assessment all in one step.

However, when there are three or more patients in line for triage, a two-step process is triggered. The next available triage nurse must do a quick 30-second interaction (ask "why are you here?" document name, etc.) and ask the patient to have a seat. Once all patients have been greeted, patients are brought back for completion of the triage process.

TIP: When there's a wait, have the patient pick up a clipboard upon entering and fill out a brief form. This will allow you to capture true time of arrival and speed up the intake process.

Exhibit 2.6

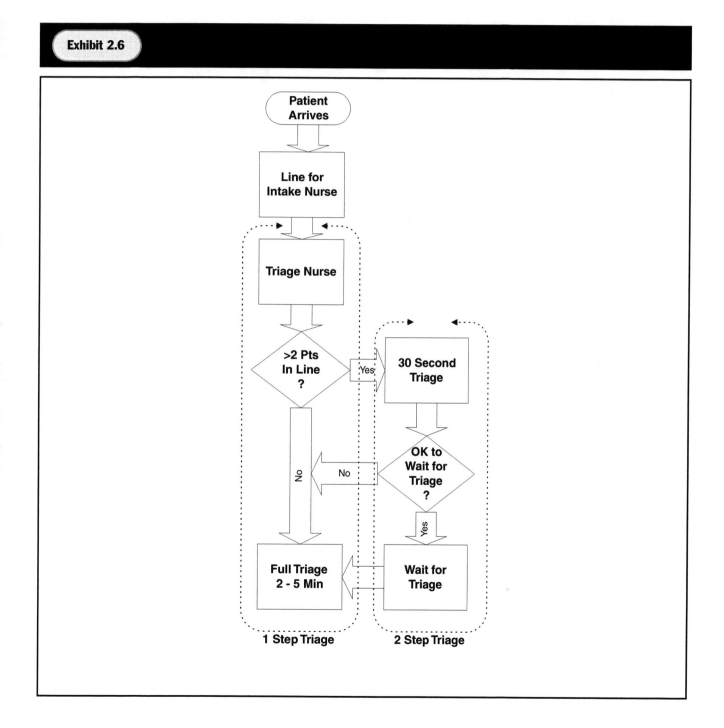

Permanent two-step triage

Some departments always have two-step triage in place (patients are always greeted by one nurse then triaged by a second nurse.) This is a warning sign of a department in trouble. It means at least one of the following:

- There is a chronic backup in triage because there are not enough triage nurses (a staffing problem)

- There is a chronic backup in triage because the triage nurses are taking too long on the triage assessment (a competency problem)

- Nursing resources are being squandered (a management problem)

→ Triggers and back-up plans

CONSIDER THIS WHEN:
- There are times when the demand for services exceeds available resources
- There is a triage team leader
- The charge nurse does not normally take a patient assignment

As in the "global" tiered response system, there can and should be tiered response systems to accommodate the normal ebb and flow of patient demand for emergency services.

There can and should be triggers for all sorts of contingencies. Here are some examples:

- **IF** more than five patients are waiting for triage, **THEN** the *triage team leader* notifies the *charge nurse,* who comes to the front to triage.

- **IF** more than 10 patients are waiting for triage, **THEN** the *charge nurse* notifies the *physician in charge,* who deploys a doctor or physician assistant to help triage.

- **IF** any urgent patient is waiting more than an hour for bed placement, **THEN** the *triage team leader* will notify the *charge nurse,* who will attempt to clear a room (either by sending a patient to the discharge area or by activating a hallway bed).

- **IF** six or more minor or nonurgent patients have waited more than one hour for care, **THEN** the *triage team leader* will notify the *charge nurse,* who will activate the virtual fast track plan.

- **IF** there is an appropriate available bed in the back and no one waiting, **THEN** the *triage nurse* will quickly collect data and place the patient in the bed within five minutes of presentation.

Note:

- The trigger should always be objective (one urgent patient waiting more than 60 minutes, 10 minor or nonurgent patients waiting more than two hours, etc.). These triggers should be set based on the needs of the patient and the standard of care in the community.

- There should always be a clearly accountable person responsible for activating the trigger.

- There should be an underlying escalation process for situations in which the backup plan does not work.

Consider trending backup plans as you would trend diversions (which is, after all, a backup plan). This could tell you something about underlying staffing levels, competencies, or other ED systems.

Communication between front and back

CONSIDER THIS WHEN:

Always

Too often within the ED we see islands of care separated by an almost total lack of information about one another. The back doesn't know what's happening in the front and the front has no idea what's happening in the back. In this section we'll discuss systems to use so that the front (triage and waiting) knows what's happening in the back (the main ED). Why is this important? Because without knowing the availability of beds in the main ED, the triage nurse cannot trigger immediate bed placement or push the next patient into the next available bed.

Knowledge of available beds in the department

There are high- and low-tech ways of getting a handle on what's happening in the back.

Camera over the white boards

One simple way to give the triage nurse a ready overview of the back end is to place a closed-circuit video camera over the white boards in the various nursing units. A split screen monitor at the triage area can then very clearly communicate the current status of each bed.

Room ready lights

One of our favorite EDs has a switch near the door of each room in the back. The switch activates a light at the triage desk to let the nurse know a bed is ready for the next patient.

ED tracking system

A high percentage of EDs have some sort of patient tracking system. If kept updated, and depending on the functionality of the system, electronic patient tracking will give an excellent real-time picture of the status in the back.

→ Triage nurse autonomy

CONSIDER THIS WHEN:
- There is good confidence in the triage process
- The triage nurse has a good idea of back-end status

Giving the triage nurse the ability to place a patient in a bed or treatment room without asking permission can make a significant difference in time to physician examination.

To implement such a system, it will be necessary to work through confidence and communication issues.

Emergent patients

There should never be a question about the placement of "emergent" patients within the ED. Even if a bed is not available, it is common practice that triage nurses bring emergent patients to the back so that, at the very least, they can be closely observed within the care setting.

Urgent patients

One ED we know of (which uses a very reliable five-level triage system) brings all urgent (level three) patients into the ED immediately. This is done, in part, because the triage nurses do not have good visibility of the waiting room and, in part, to push the nurses and physicians in the back to take on patient care responsibilities for these patients.

→ Triggers for fast track

CONSIDER THIS WHEN:

Minor and nonurgent patients must wait more than an hour to see a physician

As discussed above, it is possible to fast-track (quickly treat and discharge) a number of patients who would otherwise languish in the ED waiting room.

Process studies within some well-run EDs indicate that, although a lower-acuity patient can wait longer from a clinical standpoint, they are often seen more quickly, on average, than patients with mid-level acuities. Exhibit 2.7 shows waits for care typical at some hospitals.

Exhibit 2.7

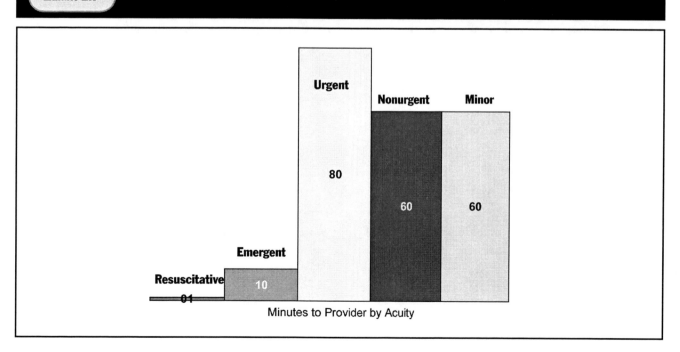

Minutes to Provider by Acuity

Why would one wish to see nonurgent and minor patients before urgent patients? It seems like heresy! But think about it: Urgent patients may need extensive work-ups and, of course, require higher-acuity care than lower-category patients. There may not be the capacity within the main ED to care for the number of urgent patients presenting. Lower-acuity patients require few services other than an exam. In the ESI, level four patients require only one service. Level five patients require nothing other than the physician or allied health examination. It is therefore easy to treat and street low acuity patients. This will clear the waiting room to allow staff to better focus on urgent patients who have yet to be seen by a physician. Also, your customers will be satisfied and the number of patients who leave without being seen will decrease.

Although we were a bit uncomfortable the first time we saw this practice in effect, upon reflection we think this is a good thing for a department struggling with throughput.

Dedicated fast track

In a perfect world, there would be enough space to build an ambulatory care area in or near the ED. The area could be staffed with a provider (physician, physician assistant, or nurse practitioner) and a technician/LPN. When open, the unit could quickly see a high number of low-acuity patients.

However, dedicated fast track units are not always open. We know of one department that is only able to open its fast-track unit about one-third of the time. In addition, dedicated fast track units require close attention from the charge nurse to maintain productivity.

Virtual fast track

Whether or not an ED has a fast track unit, a virtual fast track process should be established. Staffing a fast track function is easier than staffing a fast track unit.

As discussed above, virtual fast track would have an objective trigger and clear accountabilities. Patients may be fast tracked almost anywhere unless a complete examination is necessary, which it is probably not the case.

Here's a sample fast track function:

- The triage team leader notifies the charge nurse when 10 or more minor and nonurgent patients have waited more than an hour for bed placement.

- The charge nurse asks the physician in charge to assign a provider (physician, physician assistant, or nurse practitioner) to work with the charge nurse to fast track waiting patients.

- The charge nurse or his or her designee works with the provider to establish a location for fast tracking. Potential locations include

  - a triage examination room

  - one or two ambulatory care treatment rooms

  - a hallway within the ED

- Nonurgent and minor patients will be examined and treated as necessary in the temporary fast track area on a "next up" basis. There is one exception: At the discretion of the charge nurse or the provider, or at the request of the patient, some nonurgent or minor patients may be excluded from fast track if the temporary setting is not consistent with appropriate examination or treatment for their complaint, for example, if the patient cannot be provided privacy for the examination and care of a minor injury to the chest or lower torso.

- Fast tracking shall continue, as allowed by the needs of other patients in the department, until all nonurgent and minor patients have waited less than 30 minutes.

Remember, this is a thought stimulator only. A virtual fast track process will undoubtedly require a lot of thought, input by staff and patients, and testing.

Triage protocols

CONSIDER THIS WHEN:

Always

Take a look at the reasons patients visit your ED. A quick study will suggest which things can and should be done for patients before they see the provider. We call these triage protocols, and they have two primary functions:

- To speed up the assessment and treatment process
- To make the patient more comfortable during waits for care

⚠️ Chest pain

Chest pain is one of the most common complaints seen in the ED. It can be a symptom of a muscle strain, heart burn, or a myocardial infarction. If the patient has the latter, treatment should be swift and definitive. How does one tell? Using a chest pain protocol.

Developed in consultation with emergency medicine (EM) physicians and the critical care committee (or equivalent), a hospital's chest pain protocols are designed to quickly identify candidates for thrombolysis and decrease door-to-treatment time.

The protocol normally involves a 12-lead EKG during triage for appropriate patients, with review by a physician.

If you don't have a chest pain protocol, please develop one.

Pain

Pain is a common complaint, such as back pain, nonspecific pain, abdominal pain, ear ache, injuries (which presumably involve pain), etc.

Patients with truly severe pain will be seen right away. Other patients should have their pain treated as quickly as clinically appropriate. (Some physicians choose not to treat pain for certain presentation because doing so may mask underlying pathologies.)

Many EDs have pain protocols that are used to good effect by triage nurses.

Common interventions include oral over-the-counter pain medication, a cold pack for extremity injuries, and a recliner and a pillow.

Fever in children

Many EDs implement antipyretic protocols for children.

Imaging

Some hospitals successfully employ imaging protocols for extremity injuries. While some departments use the Ottawa (Canada) protocols successfully, others believe that they lead to overutilization and delays.

Point of care (waived) testing

Having point-of-care testing available to triage nurses is also common, since it aids the assessment of certain conditions. Common testing includes blood glucose testing, urine dip sticks, and urine pregnancy testing.

➔ Decompressing the ED

For most of this chapter, we've discussed how to cope with an onslaught of patients. However, some institutions have achieved great improvements by decreasing/diverting the volume of low-acuity patients to other settings.

CONSIDER THIS WHEN:

The ED is flooded with ambulatory care patients

We've already discussed fast track units. These can be part of the ED or can be elsewhere on the campus. As long as they are part of the hospital, the triage nurse can direct appropriate patients to the fast track unit.

However, a hospital can also take advantage of nearby nonhospital venues to decompress or reduce the volume of visits. Remember, the patients themselves must select the nonhospital setting. Once the patient has requested care at the hospital ED, EMTALA mandates that the hospital must provide the medical screening examination.

The most dramatic example we've seen involved an integrated health care delivery system where a medical group worked closely with the hospital. The ED experienced about 300 visits per day, far more than the 24-bed department could handle.

After much planning, a nonhospital urgent care center was opened near the ED. Given the option, two-thirds of the patients elected to visit the urgent care center, reducing the ED's volume by two-thirds to about 100 per day. This decompression happened virtually over night, and both the patients and the hospital won.

Keep in mind, however, that diverting patients to other venues also diverts revenue. Some ED managers say it's the less-urgent patients who pay for the sicker patients. Although this is not really true, since the hospital generally makes most of its money on admitted patients, it often seems that way to middle management due to budgetary disincentives. If you choose to provide such an option, patients must be well educated as to the limitations of the urgent care center and the capabilities of the ED. Even with education, however, the ED will get plenty of low-acuity patients, and the urgent care center will get a number of patients who require hospitalization. It is therefore essential that urgent care be staffed with highly trained caregivers and that the ED be close by, both physically and operationally.

SUBPROCESS 2

ED THROUGHPUT

Subprocess 2

ED THROUGHPUT

The emergency department (ED) throughput subprocess begins when the patient arrives inside the ED ready for a work-up and treatment. Depending on the acuity of the patient and nature of the illness, ED throughput involves the following:

- Bed placement and an initial bedside nursing assessment
- Examination by a physician, physician assistant, or nurse practitioner
- Laboratory, radiology, and other diagnostic testing
- Consultation from specialists
- Administration of medications and other treatments
- Invasive procedures

This subprocess is the most complex of the three ED subprocesses. The duration of this segment of care is dependent on the timeliness of other departments. However, when one thinks about ED overcrowding, it is the last of the subprocesses that usually comes to mind. Normally, one thinks of boarded inpatients or waiting room overflows when envisioning an overcrowded ED. However, the efficiency and timeliness of ED throughput significantly impacts the functional capacity of the department.

We know of an ED that invested significant resources on throughput. It worked on laboratory and other turnaround and consultation response times. After much effort, it reduced the average length of stay from almost six hours to a little less than three hours. By cutting the ED length of stay in half, it essentially doubled the number of patients it could see. Without adding staff or spending millions on new examination space and equipment, the department was able to increase its ability to serve the community and serve as an efficient front door to the hospital. Satisfaction and profitability skyrocketed.

A word about satisfying patients: Whenever improvements are made to ED processes and systems, satisfaction increases. Empath is a prominent health care consulting firm based in California. In its experience, patient satisfaction skyrockets along with improvements in bed placement time, throughput time, etc. Empath representatives state that satisfaction always increases proportionately to improvements in ED performance, often into the 90th percentile.

← Rotational assignments

CONSIDER THIS WHEN:

The median patient waits longer that 60 minutes for a provider

We have many people to thank as part of this work, but none more than a very wise and friendly chief of emergency medicine at a prominent Northern California hospital. He wished to improve operations in the ED, so he assembled a group of staff and let them work on the problem. His thoughts about reasons for the problem could be boiled down to long waits for care and corresponding poor patient satisfaction.

It was clear from performance data that patients tended to pile up toward the end of a provider's shift. This particular setting was unusual in that it didn't offer incentives to physicians for seeing more patients. Nevertheless, all providers worked hard. Some were faster and some were slower, but all were thorough and appropriate.

This stack of patients that accumulated toward the end of a provider's shift put the next provider on duty "behind the eight ball," often having to play catch-up for the entire shift.

The following solution worked almost immediately and cost almost nothing:

- A nurse was assigned to be the permanent partner of the physician throughout the shift.
- Each physician was given a section of "real estate" within the ED.
- Patients were assigned to the physician/nurse team at the end of triage while still in the waiting room.
- Except for the critically ill, patients were assigned on a rotational basis. If there were three

physician/nurse teams on duty, every third patient would be assigned to a given team.

- A rack system was established inside the ED, near the triage station. Patient records were placed in the rack set aside for the assigned team.
- Patients would stop being assigned to the team toward the very end of the shift.
- The physician would not leave until all his or her patients were worked up.
- Although handoffs to the next shift were allowed, they rarely happened.

The results were dramatic:

- The "bolus" of patients was no longer there for the oncoming physician
- Physicians began to work-up patients while they were still in the waiting room, sometimes ordering a test based on the triage or their nurse partner's assessments
- Wait times were reduced
- Fewer patients left without being seen (LWBS)
- Patient satisfaction increased
- Provider and staff satisfaction increased

 ## Charge nurse autonomy

CONSIDER THIS WHEN:

Always

We've spoken often about the role of the charge nurse. However, all charge nurse assignments are not created equal. Through experience we've learned that the charge nurse must have a high degree of autonomy if he or she is to be effective.

Although we're using the term "charge nurse," an assistant department manager sometimes performs some of the functions we attribute to the charge nurse. The charge nurse

- must be free of routine patient assignments.
- should have the final word when it comes to minute-by-minute operational decisions, such as when to go on diversion, when to go off diversion, when to deploy extra staff to triage, when to call in extra staff from home, etc.
- should be supported by objective, predetermined triggers and backup plans.

Charge nurse accountability for pulling patients

CONSIDER THIS WHEN:

- Charge nurses are not tied down with patient care assignments
- There are good communication systems between the triage area and the main ED
- A triage team leader has been assigned

Someone, preferably the charge nurse, should be accountable for pulling patients from the waiting room whenever a bed becomes available in the back. This obviously requires a good communication system between the front and the back. This does not necessarily have to be an ED information management system; the charge nurse or triage nurse can simply put the number of waiting patients (by triage category) on the corner of the white board whenever he or she places a patient in a bed.

 # Formalized charge nurse education program

CONSIDER THIS WHEN:

- When new charge nurses are brought on
- When charge nurse roles will change
- When charge nurses are not effectively facilitating flow

Charge nurses are not born; they are made. Moving from a patient assignment to overseeing patient flow is a natural step for some people and not quite so easy for others. Therefore, we suggest a formal education program. The program should cover the following:

- Detailed overview of department policies
- Human factors and other safety/efficiency training modules
- EMTALA
- Documentation
- Patient flow systems: intake, throughput, and output
- Patient flow priorities within each of these subprocesses
- The communication process between the charge nurse and
    - triage team leaders
    - the local EM systems agency
    - ward clerks
    - physicians
    - bed management
    - inpatient units/house supervisor

- other hospitals
- bed briefings
- consultant physicians
- Triggered response plans (e.g., triage support, call for extra staff, virtual fast track, ED boarders)
- Delegation
- Team building
- Evaluating clinical competency for triage, bedside care, and disposition
- Escalation of issues

The 'census demand curve' and staffing

CONSIDER THIS WHEN:

Always

Exhibit 3.1

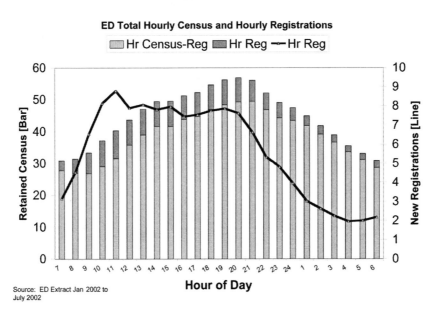

ED Total Hourly Census and Hourly Registrations

Hr Census-Reg ▓ Hr Reg ━ Hr Reg

Source: ED Extract Jan 2002 to July 2002

The bars on this chart represent the total number of patients in the department (including the waiting room). The lighter gray bars are the patients that remain in the department from previous hours. The dark "cap" on each bar indicates the new patients that have been added to the census during that hour. These numbers are repeated in the dark line (read value from axis on right) so the variation in new registrations is easily seen. This sample graph shows the typical daily flow of patients. Registrations increase quickly from 7 a.m. until peaking at 11 a.m. New registrations remain steady throughout the day, slowly tapering after 8 p.m. The total ED census lags the registrations roughly by the average length of stay. Using this graph, the ED manager can consider adding staff by staggering shifts at the beginning of the day, bringing in an extra triage nurse at 10 a.m. This extra triage nurse can shift to bedside care toward the end of the evening shift, with minimum staffing between 1 a.m. and 9 a.m.

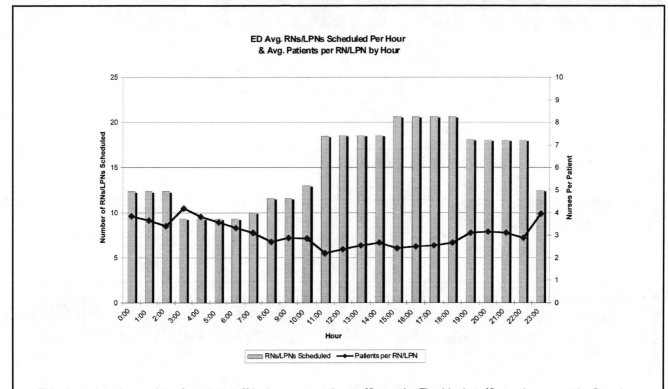

Exhibit 3.2

ED Avg. RNs/LPNs Scheduled Per Hour
& Avg. Patients per RN/LPN by Hour

RNs/LPNs Scheduled   Patients per RN/LPN

This chart plots the number of nursing staff by hour versus the staffing ratio. The ideal staffing ratio may not be flat, since more staff will be triaging and observing waiting patients between 10 a.m. and 10 p.m.

Exhibit 3.3

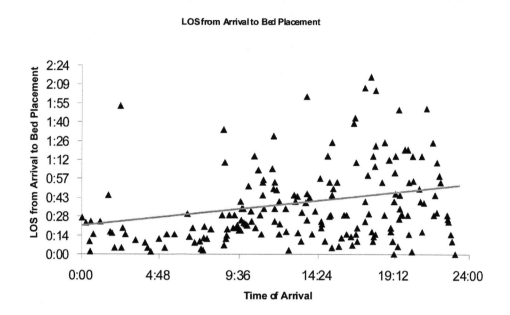

LOS from Arrival to Bed Placement

This scatter graph shows how long a random sample of patients waited for bed placement in an emergency department. The length of time patients waited for care increases as the typical day goes on. The gray "trend line" highlights the relationship between the hour of day the patient arrives and the amount of time the patient waits for care. This indicates that the department is reaching its functional capacity in the afternoon. Staffing levels is an important component of this functional capacity.

Exhibit 3.4

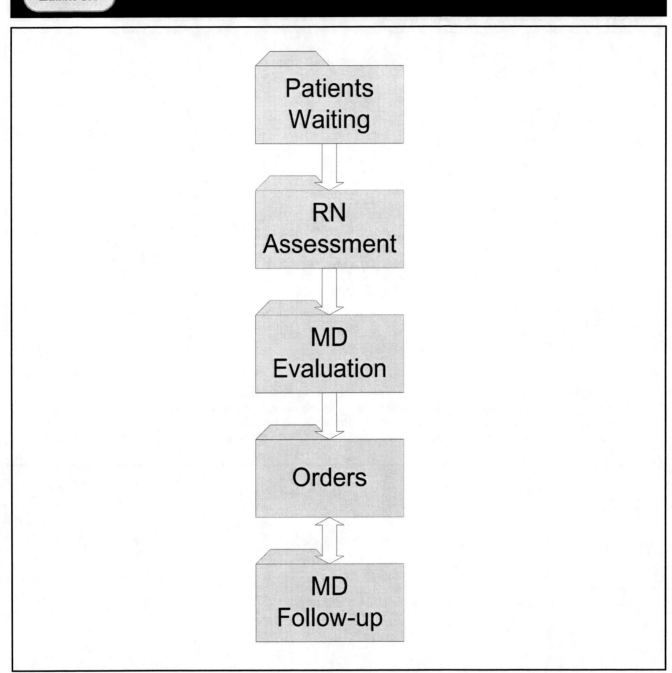

It seems so basic. All managers believe they are staffing to the workload, and most do, or at least try to. However, staffing levels and shifts are difficult to change. It is challenging to account for unsmooth patient and acuity demands in a staffing pattern.

Graphing patient demand and staffing levels can be very educational, especially to senior leadership. If the department manager is in tune with his or her department, he or she will know when staffing needs to be augmented and when it can be lightened. However, it may be difficult to explain these staffing needs to executive leadership or nursing personnel. Graphics similar to those on pp. 82–83 will help plan more precisely for staffing changes, educate leadership on the justification for staffing changes, help the manager develop a solid and justifiable budget, and demonstrate to staff how and why staggered shifts are required.

Caution: As experienced managers already know, all patients and staff are not alike. Some patients are very sick and require significant staff time; some require little more than triage and bed placement. Some staff are wonderful at the bedside, but not too great at triage. Therefore, simple plots of overall patient volumes against staffing levels usually need to be supplemented with other graphs. If there is a reliable five-tier triage system, graph hourly volume of paramedic runs by triage category and hourly volume of triages by triage category. Create a scatter diagram of time from arrival to time of bed placement by triage category. If meaningful acuity levels are assigned at the conclusion of care (in other words, if acuity scores are accurate and not every patient is assigned to one acuity level), graph hourly volume by acuity level and hourly volume of paramedic runs by acuity level. Also consider plotting volumes per hour by billing category.

A bed is a bed is a bed

CONSIDER THIS WHEN:

Always

Some departments are designed with small modules: one for pediatric patients, one for cardiac patients, one for general medical patients, one for ambulatory patients, etc. If you are in the process of designing a new or remodeled department, please do not do this.

The logic usually goes like this: "We have a large number of [pediatric, cardiac, trauma, etc.] patients and it would be far better to manage them all in the same location [true]. Therefore we should dedicate four beds for [children, chest pain, etc.] patients." If you actually build small modules for various patient populations, however, experience has taught us that you will not be happy with the results.

- Small modules are expensive for staff because patient-to-nurse ratios are frequently higher than necessary, based on a patient's changing acuity levels
- Cross coverage is difficult
- It is rare that the average number of patients is ever in the department

Therefore, make the following commitments and lead a happy life:

- Design or deploy beds in modules of 12–16 beds.

- Accommodate specific patient types in the design (e.g., isolation patients, trauma patients, psychiatric patients, observation patients, etc.) without limiting the use of such rooms to those patients. A module designed primarily for ambulatory care should nevertheless have rooms that are suitable for gurney patients (either no walls to the nursing unit or glass walls that can slide out of the way when necessary). Observation beds should be designed just like ED beds, but with different equipment (i.e., inpatient beds v. gurneys).

- Although few believe they will need temporary bed spaces when planning a brand new unit, think about where excess gurney patients can be safely placed when reviewing the new design.

- Have multiple rooms appropriate for the assessment and management of gynecological complaints.

- Have rooms that can function as eye examination rooms when needed.

- Have rooms that can function as general exam and treatment spaces during the day and psychiatric observation spaces at night.

- Even though you have or are planning to have an electronic patient information system, make sure there is central wall space for a white board, just in case.

The bottom line: Patient flow and populations change day to day and year to year, and the assumptions made at the beginning of a design process rarely fit the true scenario by the time beds are built. Circumstances will certainly change (patient population, demand, staffing, physician model, etc.) over the life of the unit. Therefore, to the extent possible, try to insist on a model that will not tie your hands by making certain beds appropriate for only one patient type. Make multiple rooms appropriate for many uses. In short, keep the mantra "a room is a room is a room" in mind, even though, strictly speaking, this will never be completely true.

Direct bed placement

CONSIDER THIS WHEN:

Always

Although we've discussed this before (see Subprocess 1), we've placed this flag under the "ED throughput" subprocess because placing a patient directly in the bed will require some preparation by the folks in the back. There must be a system for quickly assessing patients who are directly placed in a bed. Remember, they may not have been triaged yet and they may have a significant complaint that requires immediate attention.

Be aware of "patient hoarding" practices—essentially dragging one's feet about discharging a patient to delay getting the next one. Staff do this to give themselves a breather, and while breathers are important (and make for better care), patient hoarding is not the way to get one. Having a good white board system and effective charge nurses is essential if direct bed placement is to be implemented.

 ## Utilization of ancillary services

CONSIDER THIS WHEN:

- The average length of stay for all ED patients is more than three hours
- The average length of stay for discharged patients is more than 2.5 hours

The ordering of unnecessary or excessive tests delays patient throughput, artificially raises triage levels when using the ESI or similar triage scales, and is frowned upon by third-party payers.

In this book, we're mostly concerned about the first consideration.

We recommend two approaches to dealing with this growing problem:

1. Develop protocols by collaborating with the laboratory and imaging departments to help guide physician practice

2. Develop protocols for nursing so physicians can make the decision to test earlier rather than later

Chest pain protocols, for example, should always be in place. Protocols for other complaints, such as those for diabetic patients, abdominal patients, intoxicated patients, etc., can help physicians and staff get the right test the first time rather than having to wait for follow-up testing.

Testing, along with productivity, should be profiled by the physician for use by the contract group in monitoring care. We strongly recommend that this issue be left to physician peer review. However, having a good medical group to manage the ED generally comes with outstanding peer review capabilities.

⊕ Physician staffing and qualifications

CONSIDER THIS WHEN:

Always

EM is a relatively new specialty. Therefore, there may not be enough good EM physicians to go around. There are occasions when a generalist is not available, but we strongly recommend that at least one EM physician be on duty at all times. If only one EM specialist is on duty, he or she should be the physician in charge. This is a form of qualifications smoothing, and is preferable to staffing with a matrix of specialties (adult medicine, pediatrics, surgery, etc.) that are not comfortable with all patient types.

⊕ Complaint/condition driven documentation systems

CONSIDER THIS WHEN:

Physician documentation is an issue

Many departments use complaint-specific physician documentation systems (e.g., the "T" System) because it helps

- remind the physician of the necessary assessment steps
- plan care and treatment, since it locates findings in a standard place on the record
- physician documentation, since some parts of the assessment require documentation to justify reimbursement ("if it's not documented, it wasn't done")

Some of these systems have been around for a long time and work well. However, some clinicians are more comfortable with an "open" documentation system because it may better capture the uniqueness of a patient's history and physical findings.

Some new electronic documentation systems are beginning to merge the best of both worlds, combining condition/complaint-specific cues, common text notation, and limited free text, all displayed in a dictation-like format that is immediately available. These systems show great promise.

Phlebotomy

CONSIDER THIS WHEN:

- The average time from laboratory test order to completion is longer than 45 minutes (median)
- The median time from laboratory test order to receipt of the specimen in the laboratory is longer than 15 minutes

Some medical centers have significantly reduced specimen collection time by having someone other than the bedside nurse available and accountable for blood draws. Although this person can be a phlebotomist on loan from the laboratory, it is best to have a trained technician whose blood draws are supervised by the laboratory, but who can perform other ED tech duties. This allows more hours of phlebotomy coverage during the days.

Temporary bed locations

CONSIDER THIS WHEN:

- There are times when demand for ED services exceeds the bed supply
- Admitted patients are routinely "boarded" in the ED. (We define boarding as retaining admitted patients for longer than the routine admission turnaround time due to lack of an inpatient bed.)

We strongly recommend that you mark temporary bed locations (sometimes called hallway beds) on the wall next to the bed location. Make sure the bed does not obstruct the department's exit. Accommodate these temporary beds on the white board, and establish objective triggers for use of the hallway beds, for example, five urgent patients have waited longer than 30 minutes for bed placement.

Chart rack system

CONSIDER THIS WHEN:

Always

Every department has a chart flow system—charts with pending nursing orders go here, charts with imaging orders go there, etc. However, it is very important that there be an easily visible rack system (even if there's an automated tracking system installed). This allows the ward clerk, patient care nurse, physician, and charge nurse to see from across the room whether something is pending.

Here's a sample chart rack system for inside the main ED, in the usual order of care:

- Rack for waiting patients organized by triage category (often in the triage area)
- Rack for patients just placed in beds who need a nursing assessment
- Rack for patients ready for the initial physician examination (see box below about options for the order of care)
- Rack for pending orders, often subdivided by imaging, radiology, and nursing (i.e., medications)
- Rack for physician reexamination (i.e., new results, etc.)

It is usually effective to combine the initial examination and reexamination racks into one two-shelf box for each physician. Use the upper box for new patients and the lower box when results are received.

NEW THINKING ABOUT THE ORDER OF CARE

Some new thinkers envision a nonsequential system for ED care. ED leaders are experimenting with novel systems based on the concept that patients need to be seen in sequence. For example, when a patient presents for care at the front door he or she can be escorted to an open bed where, depending on who's available, the physician can see the patient to begin the exam, the nurse can see the patient for an assessment, or the ward clerk can see the patient for registration. This is a promising thought and has potential for speeding things along. However, if you are considering this, be prepared to deal with a number of complex issues, such as patient banding for identification, triage, interior waiting areas, and staff smoothing.

This nonlinear care model depends on electronic and traditional/manual cues, such as chart rack systems.

→ Flags for ambulatory beds

CONSIDER THIS WHEN:

• The ED has a separate unit or dedicated beds for ambulatory care
• The length of stay for discharged patients is longer than 2.5 hours

EDs often use lights or flags above doors to prompt staff that the rooms are empty. A formal system is highly recommended when there are enclosed ambulatory care spaces within the department.

Some departments install colored plastic "railroad" flags outside the exam room door. If the green flag is up, the room is vacant. If the yellow flag is up, the patient is ready for discharge. If the blue flag is up, the patient is ready for the physician exam.

Other departments have a simple light system: A green light means the room is empty, a white light means the physician is with the patient, and a red light means the patient needs assistance.

→ Computer tracking systems

CONSIDER THIS WHEN:

The department already has a good manual tracking system

We've spoken at length about computer tracking systems. However, we want to be very clear about when they are effective and when they are not effective for managing the main ED.

- A computer can automate a good flow process, but it cannot create one. Therefore, first have a good white board system, a good chart rack system, and a strong charge nurse function.
- Getting data from the system is easy. Analyzing the data and turning them into information will take analytical resources.
- If a computer is to replace the white board, make certain the displays are large and located in such a way that they can be conveniently viewed.
- Remember that, to be useful, information must be readily visible to a number of staff members. Don't put unnecessary clinical information on the displays, since it could compromise the patient's right to confidentiality and privacy.

White board system

CONSIDER THIS WHEN:

Always

MYTH BUSTERS

It is a common myth that patient names may not be used on a white board inside the emergency department. This is simply not true. In fact, being able to quickly identify patient locations is essential to safe and efficient operations. This myth is based, however, on the experience of some departments with inaccurate findings and surveyor interpretations during JCAHO or DHS surveys. To guard yourself against inaccurate findings, and to resolve issues that have already arisen, follow a few simple rules (also see Appendix B "Use and Placement of White Boards,"

1. Do the right thing: Make sure your system is truly in the best interest of the patient

2. Say what you do, then do what you say: Have a very simple statement

---

Once confidentiality issues are accommodated, the white board should have the information that best addresses the flow issues in your department. Each department is different, but in general we recommend the following:

- A row for each bed and space, including routinely used "temporary" locations
- Patient last name and first initial
- Name of primary nurse assignment
- Time of arrival
- Time of bed placement
- Time of admission order (these times are important so that the patient's stay and care process can be viewed at a glance)
- Responsible physician
- Flag that the patient has been examined by a physician
- Flags or codes for radiology tests pending, patient out of department, consultations pending, and other indications
- A flag for bed turnover (e.g., a red magnet indicating that the room/bed space is now empty or the patient's name is erased once the room is ready for the next bed placement)

- Number of patients waiting for bed placement by acuity
- Diversion status

The white board should be updated by the patient care nurse or anyone else with current information about the patient. The charge nurse or triage team leader should be accountable for updating the number of waiting patients. The physician should be accountable for updating physician examination information. The charge nurse should be accountable for updating diversion status.

ACCOUNTABILITY

Note the frequent use of the words "accountable" and "accountability." It is our opinion that unless accountabilities are clear and unambiguous, the relevant system is not a system at all; it's merely an idea.

Never design a process or implement a policy that does not have specific accountabilities. Say, "The patient care nurse shall . . ." or the "ward clerk will . . ."

- Do not say, "The time of inpatient bed request shall be entered in the column marked 'A' on the white board" unless you complete the sentence by saying "by the ward clerk."
- If more than one person is relied upon for a certain function, both should be held accountable. For example, "The charge nurse AND the triage team leader are accountable for updating the number of waiting patients." Do not use "the charge nurse OR the triage team leader."
- Establish time frames for the accountabilities. Say, "The ward clerk shall put the results in the chart within five minutes of receipt from the laboratory."
- Accumulate all the various position accountabilities in one location, perhaps an attachment to or part of the job description, and give it to the employee. Make certain they know their accountabilities.
- Make certain that the charge nurse knows the entire matrix of accountabilities.
- Make certain, finally, that the department manager is accountable for clearly defining accountabilities.

➔ Performance contracts with suppliers

CONSIDER THIS WHEN:

Always

We often hear departments complain about laboratory or radiology turnaround times, or about how long it takes for a consultant to arrive. We then talk to the respective department or clinical service and hear a different story.

There is really only one answer: reliable, accurate, mutually agreed-upon performance data.

Agree with laboratory and radiology on an overall performance metric. The measure should include all parts of the process, although it will probably be subdivided according to accountability. For example, measure the entire time from the order for a laboratory test to the posting of the result in the chart. Then and only then should subdividing be allowed (e.g., from order to specimen, from specimen to accession, from accession to result).

Both departments should use the same data to report to senior leadership. Performance targets should be agreed upon when a problem is noted. Most of the time, performance will only improve when both departments are involved and accountable for the improvement process.

For physician turnaround (i.e., consultation requests), be certain to record in the medical record the time the physician was first contacted. Then merely track and trend the data by clinical service and physician, and give the information to the chief of emergency services. He or she can then discuss the performance in appropriate settings.

→ Satellite laboratory services

CONSIDER THIS WHEN:
- Time from the order for laboratory testing to the time the results are posted averages more than 45 minutes during busy times
- Patient volume exceeds 50,000 annual visits

Although we say to consider a satellite lab when the patient volume is more than 50,000 visits, this is just a rough rule of thumb. In fact, the need for a satellite laboratory will almost entirely be driven by the kind of equipment available and the volume of testing.

We find that many laboratories are able to perform best if there is a virtual STAT lab within the department—for example, all samples from the ED are delivered to the same location: within the main laboratory. Dedicated staff then manage these tests within the lab.

This is a complex subject, and should ultimately be driven by performance data that reflect overall testing turnaround times, as well as turnaround times on specific, high-profile tests (i.e., troponin levels).

⊙ Satellite radiology services

CONSIDER THIS WHEN:
- The average time from order to film is more than 45 minutes
- There is a high volume of patients with orthopedic injuries

Some hospitals are ready to install a dedicated computed tomography scanning unit. We prefer that the unit be placed in the imaging department, but near the busy ED.

Many departments with high volumes of simple films have found it very effective to have satellite imaging capabilities.

⊙ Automatic requests for medical records

CONSIDER THIS WHEN:
Always

We see no reason to wait for the charge nurse or physician to request prior medical records from the health information management (HIM) department. These requests should be made automatically upon patient registration.

⊙ Pneumatic tubes

CONSIDER THIS WHEN:
Always

There are two functions for a pneumatic tube system.

The first is for delivery of medical records from the chart room to the ED (and throughout the hospital). The only replacement for this system in our minds is a fully functional, complete electronic medical record.

The second use of a pneumatic tube is delivery of laboratory specimens from the ED (and other units for STAT laboratory work) to the laboratory. This allows the creation of a virtual STAT laboratory within the main lab.

Equipment and medications

CONSIDER THIS WHEN:

Always

There is often tension between the ED and departments such as materials management or the pharmacy. Materials management wants to drive down inventory costs, and therefore tends to rely on just-in-time supplies, which doesn't really work for the ED. In addition, JCAHO requires a pharmacist's review prior to the first dose of most medications in the hospital. There is an exception for patients being actively treated by a physician in the emergency department. (JCAHO speaks of a "physician-controlled environment.")

It is therefore incumbent upon the ED to work with both materials management and the pharmacy to establish PAR levels for medications and supplies that will not impede efficient operations.

Automated medication dispensing machines are becoming very common in EDs to better manage this need.

Sub-waiting areas

CONSIDER THIS WHEN:

- Urgent patients (in a five-level system) sometimes wait longer than 30 minutes for bed placement
- Emergent patients are not always placed in a bed immediately

Most EDs experience times when higher acuity patients may have to wait longer for care than is ideal. In such cases, we feel it is essential to establish a high-acuity waiting area or process. There are several options:

- The high-acuity waiting area can be near the triage area. However, if it is, the area should be located in such a way that it preserves patient dignity and privacy while allowing convenient observation by the triage nurse(s).

- Some departments bring all urgent patients directly into the main ED. If the patient has to wait, he or she will wait directly across from the nursing station. This approach has only been taken when there is an appropriate location nearby the nursing station for patients to wait and there is not a good alternative for the close observation of urgent patients.

Preprinted orders

CONSIDER THIS WHEN:

Always

There is a trend toward translating high-risk or common order sets into preprinted orders for a number of reasons:

- The physician can be reminded up-front of commonly agreed upon diagnostic studies and interventions for various situations. The most common sets of preprinted orders relate to conditions such as cardiac chest pain.
- There is less potential for misunderstanding or misreading physician orders, leading to fewer requests for clarification and fewer potential medication errors.
- In some cases, a preprinted admission order set has been developed in order to avoid boarding patients due to delays in admission work-ups. These orders would be used when the attending physician or team would assume responsibility for the ongoing treatment plan shortly after placement on the inpatient unit (four to six hours).

Observation patients

CONSIDER THIS WHEN:

Always

Clinical decision units within the ED

Some patients need to be observed as part of the EM work-up. Will a given medication alleviate the symptoms? How will the patient respond to breathing treatments? What effect will rehydration have on the patient?

This type of observation stay is usually less than four hours, and is billed as part of the ED medical screening examination.

It is usually best to keep the patient in the original bed for such short-term clinical decision-making. Moving these patients from the bed to an observation unit often delays the ultimate disposition.

Longer-term observation

There are other patients who will require a formal "observation" stay of up to 24 hours. Medicare rules for such observations are clear. There are two types of units that have been used for such observation: those attached to the ED and those in inpatient beds.

Units that are attached to the ED have the advantage of a nearby physician who can attend to patients. It also has a theoretical ED mindset, which will likely manage the observation more quickly. Unfortunately, these observation units sometimes fail for the following reasons:

- Physicians are appropriately more focused on incoming patients rather than actively managing the observation stay.
- Precious space is taken from the pool or space available to handle the incoming.
- Formal observation patients are expected to receive inpatient-like care. Medications require a pharmacist's prereview, and an observation work-up (history and physical examination) should be in the chart.

Observation units on the inpatient floor in inpatient beds are theoretically ideal. Patients who end up staying longer than expected can be converted to inpatients or extended to 48 hours of observation without a change in location. However, some hospitals have had problems with these units:

- Attending physicians or teams may not be readily available to care for the patient, and the patients are too far away from the ED to enable efficient physician coverage
- An inpatient mindset may drive slower work-ups and assessments than would occur were the unit located in or managed by the ED

➔ When does EMTALA allow the collection of billing information?

CONSIDER THIS WHEN:
Always

EMTALA requires that medical screening not be delayed to obtain financial information. California (and perhaps some other states) prohibits the practice of looking up financial information until after the medical screening examination. Also, some patients may leave without being seen if billing issues are raised too early in the care process. On the other hand, obtaining accurate billing information is essential to the financial health of the organization and the department.

We recommend a relatively conservative approach: A business services or billing representative should not approach the patient until the provider's first examination. This is not a hard-and-fast rule for states without an EMTALA Plus rule for billing. However, it is recommended because of hard experience with interactions between billing staff and patients who may require prompt care and treatment without appropriate clinical input and judgment.

Pediatric dosing aids

CONSIDER THIS WHEN:
Always

Before we leave Subprocess 2, we would like to mention a number of devices used to assist physicians and nurses in giving the right doses to pediatric patients during crises. Some companies sell very useful tapes that convert an infant's length to a presumed weight, for medication dosing and for use in the selection of tubes and other equipment. They are becoming the standard of care, and there are few departments without them.

However, we urge that you take the next step. Some children's hospitals have developed a calculation tool for emergency medications that allow nurses to quickly retrieve the correct dose of medication during a code or other urgent situation. These tools can be as simple as a grid with weights/lengths across the top and standard dosage calculations across the middle (amount per kilogram should always appear independently on the tool). Some have proposed putting these into handheld devices (i.e., personal digital assistants).

We encourage hospitals' shock and resuscitation committees (or equivalent) to consider implementing these tools. However, we also urge consistency, so that all responding to the code can know what to expect, regardless of their location in the hospital.

SUBPROCESS 3

ED OUTPUT

Subprocess 3

ED OUTPUT

ED output, or disposition, should be quite simple. (See Exhibit 4.1.) The patient has been seen and diagnosed, and a treatment plan developed. The hard part is over, right? Perhaps. However, there are many kinks along the path to the back door of the ED.

There are three disposition types:

- Discharges to home
- Transfers to another institution
- Admission to an inpatient or observation unit

Exhibit 4.1

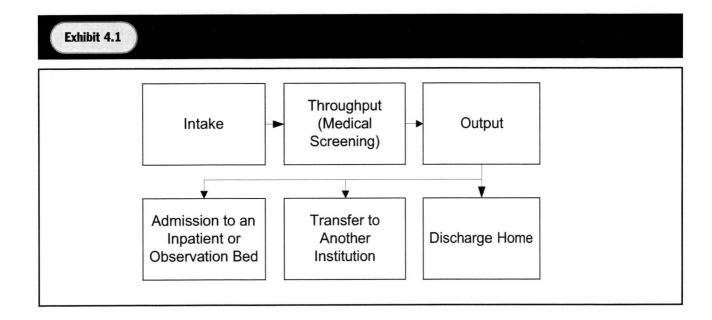

→ Eliminate unnecessary loop-backs and assessments when discharging patients to their homes

CONSIDER THIS WHEN:

There are unnecessary delays in the patient discharge process

---

EMTALA CLARIFICATION:

Remember EMTALA? It requires medical screening and stabilization. CMS has defined two types of stabilization: one for transfer and one for discharge. Once the patient is shown to be stabilized, EMTALA obligations end.

Stability for discharge involves two elements:

- Documenting that the patient has reached a state in his or her care process in which he or she can continue care in an ambulatory setting (i.e., a physician's office), or on an inpatient basis in the future (e.g., the patient may safely return to the hospital later for an open fracture reduction).
- This appropriate plan for follow-up care must be documented as part of the discharge instructions.

Out of concern for potential EMTALA violations, some EDs have insisted that a patient return to the ED following a closed fracture reduction at a nearby medical office. This should not be required, as long as the

- fracture was appropriately stabilized (i.e., splint)
- patient understood the time frame in which the reduction should take place
- patient understood how to get the fracture reduced within that time frame
- record reflects appropriate pain control and lack of neurovascular compromise

Although this example involves an orthopedic patient, the same principle can be applied to eye cases and other situations in which the patient is handed off to other providers for definitive treatment. In other words, when the patient leaves the department, your care process should be complete.

➔ Discharge documentation tool

CONSIDER THIS WHEN:
- There are unnecessary delays in the patient discharge process
- It takes the typical nurse more than five minutes to discharge a patient

Develop a quick and simple documentation tool that assists nurses in performing quick but complete discharge assessments. Remember to prompt the nurse to document the following elements:

- Observations/assessments related to presenting complaint. For example, if the patient was in pain at presentation, record his or her pain level at the time of discharge. If the patient was nauseated at presentation, document whether he or she was nauseated at discharge.

- Some departments make taking vital signs at discharge, including pain, mandatory. This is not necessarily required for all patients, so consider the competence and performance of your nursing staff and the severity of illness of the average discharged patients. Discharge vital signs should only be necessary when indicated.

- How and with whom did they leave? Did they go home with a friend or did they leave in a taxi?

- Document the patient's understanding of discharge instructions, including his or her plan for follow-up care.

- Consider developing a discharge instruction documentation tool that can be retained as a part of the medical record.

All of these elements should be simple to use.

➔ Communication for shift bed turnover

CONSIDER THIS WHEN:
It takes more than five minutes after discharge for the bed to be ready for the next patient

As we stated earlier, communication is the key to improving most processes throughout the hospital. Lack of a consistent, easy-to-use communication system will lead to unnecessary delays that will impede flow and in some cases harm patients.

ED bed turnover is a perfect example of how communication can help, especially if housekeeping is involved in the turnover process.

A very strong visual cue on the white board or tracking system should indicate when a patient was discharged or has left the bed for a centralized discharge area (see below). The charge nurse and others will then know that turnover is pending.

Also, consider making nursing responsible for most bed turnover procedures in order to eliminate a potentially unnecessary handoff that could delay bed placement.

⊛ Discharge area

CONSIDER THIS WHEN:

There are unnecessary delays in the patient's discharge to home

Most departments experience delays during certain times in discharging patients to their homes. When the issue becomes chronic, it may be time to look for a discharge waiting location.

Patients who are ready to go home but still need instruction or a last-minute nursing check can wait (briefly) in a dedicated location, to allow nursing personnel to perform necessary discharge functions without delaying bed placement for incoming patients.

However, a racking system or white board cue will be necessary to ensure appropriate cues and avoid potential communication problems.

⚠ Preprinted discharge instructions

CONSIDER THIS WHEN:

Always

Preprinted, conveniently available discharge instructions are essential for some complaints. However, make sure that the pre-printed instructions are available in the languages commonly spoken by your patients and have content approved by the physician chief of the ED.

 Observation units

 CONSIDER THIS WHEN:

There are indications that the ED needs to be decompressed, for example:

- The hospital diverts paramedic ambulances more than 40 hours per month
- There are usually more than four inpatients being boarded (held for lack of an available inpatient bed) in the ED
- Temporary bed locations appear permanent

We are strong advocates of abundant observation beds in separate observation units. Although observation units do not free up inpatient beds directly, they may decrease the demand for inpatient beds, and observation units certainly free up space in the ED, thereby increasing its "functional capacity."

How do we distinguish between observation and clinical decision-making? For the sake of discussion, join us in accepting the following distinctions:

- Clinical decision-making is a very brief period (usually less than six hours) during which the patient's condition is observed primarily to aid in the diagnostic work-up.

- Observation is a mini-hospitalization. The diagnosis has been made and the treatment plan anticipates a stay of less than 24 hours. There is an observation order set accompanied by an observation history and physical examination (usually a short-form history and physical or a long physician progress note).

As mentioned before, we recommend that clinical decision-making take place in the main treatment area of the ED, normally in the bed (or gurney) assigned upon admission to the unit. On the other hand, we feel strongly that observation should take place in a separate unit, where nursing care can be provided on a more predictable basis, medication regimens can be completely reviewed by a pharmacist, etc.

We observe a direct relationship between overcrowding in the ED and lack of sufficient observation space. After a little reflection, it's not difficult to see why these two are related. Without available observation beds, some patients remain in the clinical decision-making mode for a long time—often far longer than the normal four to six hour window. In addition, if it comes to a choice between managing an observation patient in the main ED or an inpatient bed, the patient will be managed in the ED for the following reasons:

- Patients stay longer in a traditional inpatient unit than in either the ED or a dedicated observation unit

- Billing for an observation stay in a traditional inpatient unit does not "pencil out"

- There is a shortage of open inpatient units

Let's assume you're convinced that having an observation unit is a good thing. What then? Consider the following for locating and staffing an observation unit:

- If the ED physician will attend observation patients, the unit should be located in or near the ED. It is neither safe nor efficient to pull physicians staffing the ED away from the unit—both observation and emergency patient populations will suffer.

- If a team of hospital rounding specialists or other identified physicians will be actively managing the observation patients, then the observation unit should be located away from the ED.

If the observation unit will be located away from the ED, look for a closed medical/surgical unit with licensed but unused inpatient beds. Locating observation in licensed inpatient beds allows the convenient conversion to inpatient status when warranted by changes in the patient's condition.

 ## Case management and discharge planning

CONSIDER THIS WHEN:

Always

COMMON TYPES OF CASES THAT INVOLVE MANAGEMENT/DISCHARGE PLANNING IN ED OUTPUT

- All transfers to other institutions
- Delays in arrangements for required follow-up care (e.g., treadmill, MRI, etc.)
- Inadequate financial resources
- History of noncompliance with medical instruction (i.e., "frequent flyers")
- Patients with chronic diseases, such as COPD, HIV/AIDS, hypertension, and asthma (for potential placement in care management programs)
- CVA/stroke patients or other serious impairment of activities of daily living

---

We will discuss the virtues of case management for inpatients a bit later in the book. However, it is difficult to overstate the importance of an effective case management program to the well-being of the ED.

Although we discuss case management here in the "output" section of the ED subprocesses, case management should ideally start during intake. An effective case manager can and should intervene in all of an ED's difficult or complex patient placements.

The following are aspects of an effective ED case management program:

- A case manager should be assigned or readily available to the ED seven days a week.

- ED case management hours should match the need (by hour of day and day of week), which will not normally be 9 a.m. to 5 p.m., Monday through Friday. Some of the most difficult placement issues happen in the middle of the night (psychiatric patients, chemically dependent patients, homeless patients, etc.).

- The case manager should be notified as soon as it becomes apparent that there may be difficulty in placing a patient after medical screening.

Other locations for boarded patients

CONSIDER THIS WHEN:

Admitted patients are consistently held in the ED due to the lack of an inpatient bed

According to many in the emergency medicine community, patients should never be boarded in the ED. Emergency personnel argue that if the patient can stay in the hallway of the ED, he or she can stay in the hallway of the telemetry or ICU.

JCAHO has adopted some of this thinking by requiring hospitals to plan for the best location for the patient rather than merely assuming that place to be the ED.

So what are some reasonable alternatives for boarded patients?

Post anesthesia care units

The post anesthesia care unit (PACU) is always a likely candidate for boarders. (See Exhibit 4.2.)

Exhibit 4.2

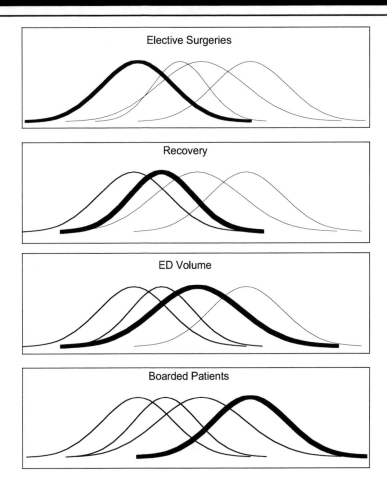

This graphic depicts the staggered operational flows of patients that usually make the post anesthesia recovery area available for patient boarding. These graphs are not intended to represent the true shape of the demand curves for the various areas and services. They merely show that peak demand times are sequenced throughout the day. The PACU is busy until mid afternoon, which is when the number of boarded patients also rises. (Coincidentally, this also illuminates the relationship between elective surgery and ED overcrowding . . . the number of ED boarders tends to increase as inpatient beds are filled with patients following elective surgery.)

As the picture on this page depicts, recovery beds are typically beginning to empty just as the number of boarders begins to increase. The recovery room has monitored beds and open architecture to facilitate care for various kinds of patients. However, the PACU's open design does not provide an optimal environment for inpatients. In addition, the surgery schedule will begin to compete with inpatient boarders by midmorning.

Inpatient units

There are those who question why patients can be (supposedly) safely boarded in the ED hallway but not in the hallway of the telemetry or ICUs. This is a difficult question. On one hand, the ED and its staff are used to "hallway beds." On the other hand, inpatient nursing is more comfortable with the extensive order set of the typical inpatient. Consider a compromise: send inpatient nurses to the ED to care for boarded patients.

 Transfer packs

CONSIDER THIS WHEN:

Always

Transferring a patient to another institution is risky from a compliance point of view. There are many crucial pieces of information to collect for regulatory risk management purposes. Consider the following:

- A stock of interhospital transfer packets containing all necessary documents should be maintained

- The charge nurse should review the paperwork at the time of each transfer to ensure completeness

- The nurse should briefly assess the patient for stability when he or she is ready to leave

- The physician should make a brief note of the patient's condition just before transfer (ideally within 15 minutes of transfer)

Some institutions have developed a one-page transfer summary. Appendix B is a sample of such a form.

The form contains the following:

- The patient's agreement to be transferred
- The physician's statement as to the stability of the patient and the risks and benefits of the transfer
- Information about who accepted the transfer at the receiving institution
- Spaces for last-minute checks of the patient's condition prior to transfer

---

MYTH BUSTER

Lateral transfers for financial reasons are not prohibited by EMTALA.

It is a common misunderstanding that EMTALA only allows the transfer of patients to other institutions because a) they require care or services not available at the sending hospital or b) the patient requests the transfer. What many forget is that a hospital's obligation under EMTALA is to stabilize the patient. Once stabilized, EMTALA rules no longer govern.

EMTALA considers a patient stable for transfer if the treating physician at the sending hospital believes the patient's clinical condition is not likely to deteriorate during the transfer.

Once a patient is stable for transfer, the transfer can be made for continuity of care or other purposes. For example, with the permission of the patient, he or she may be "repatriated" to an institution within his or her health plan network or, for medically indigent patients, to institutions reimbursed for their care.

Therefore, can a hospital transfer a patient for financial reasons? Yes, but the following considerations apply:

- The transfer must be truly clinically appropriate and safe
- The patient must consent to the transfer
- Some states (i.e., California) have laws to address this issue. It is therefore advisable to address the transfer in terms of continuity of care.
- Some hospitals are obliged to care for the medically indigent and therefore may be prohibited from finding other homes for such inpatients.
- There are not a lot of hospitals willing to accept lateral transfers if the patient has no funds. Whether the hospital can legally transfer the patient may be trumped by the reality of our crumbling health care safety net.

Discharge packs/resources

CONSIDER THIS WHEN:

Always

Similar to transfer packs, a stock of discharge forms should also be maintained. An up-to-date list of outside health care resources should be included, along with pre-printed discharge instructions (mentioned earlier). This resource list will help the institution demonstrate, as required, that discharged patients are given an appropriate plan for follow-up care as part of their discharge instructions.

Paper flow

CONSIDER THIS WHEN:

Always

Paper documentation systems have a significant limitation in that only one person can possess a given medical records form at any given time. Because more than one person is usually engaged in diagnosing and treating a patient's condition, the chart tends to become fragmented: physicians have their notes, and nurses have theirs.

This separation of forms is not an optimal system, but it seems to be the norm. It is therefore very important to establish a consistent paperwork flow process so that elements of the documentation may be found when needed. In addition, all elements of the chart should be brought together at the earliest possible convenience—certainly no later than the patient's discharge.

SUBPROCESS 4

INPATIENT INTAKE

Subprocess 4

INPATIENT INTAKE

The inpatient intake (or admission) process is among the most complex and problem-prone systems in health care. Many ED overcrowding issues can be traced to these processes and to the numerous hand-offs between the admission order and the actual admission.

→ Handoffs and communication

CONSIDER THIS WHEN:

Inpatient admissions take longer than an hour to process

We mentioned that a good source of quick, tangible improvements is the communication process between departments or units. The inpatient admission process is replete with handoffs and, in most institutions, missed communications.

Here are some steps to follow when trying to improve this subprocess:

- Do not proceed until accurate data are collected and aggregated on each admission. At a very minimum, times from admission order to inpatient bed placement must be collected. These data must be clean and readily available to the improvement team.
- Consider conducting a modified Failure Modes and Effects Analysis (FMEA) on the communication process during admissions. Whereas the FMEA discussed by the Joint Commission on Accreditation of Healthcare Organizations (JCAHO) is meant to focus on and improve patient safety, it can work well for debugging clinical systems to improve flow.
- Flow chart the process after interviewing ED physicians, attending physicians, ED nurses, inpatient nurses, inpatient ward clerks, ED ward clerks, transporters, environmental services representatives,

business services representatives, financial counselors, pharmacists, dietitians, and nurse managers.

- Assign the risk of significant delay should a breakdown in communication take place.
- For high-risk items, outline potential reasons for the miscommunication.
- Consider eliminating some steps in the admission process.
- Consider performing some steps in parallel, rather than sequentially.
- Try changing the process for high-risk communications that have poor performance levels, and quickly measure the results.
- If the results are positive, permanently implement the changed process.
- If the results are inconclusive or negative, go back to the old system and move on to another potential communication step improvement.

 **Bed ahead**

CONSIDER THIS WHEN:

Inpatient admissions take longer than an hour to process

The "bed ahead" system is espoused by a number of hospital throughput experts. In this system, first determine the median number of admissions per shift (or hour) and per day requested from the ED, from the OR, and other sources. This median number becomes the working target for the bed coordinator (as opposed to waiting for the actual request to be made). As these beds are filled, the bed coordinator must try to ensure that at least one additional bed is available for the unit, thereby keeping a "bed ahead."

 Bed tracking

CONSIDER THIS WHEN:

Always

A good bed-tracking process is essential. All hospitals have a system of some sort. And it is surprising to learn how unreliable some of the bed-tracking systems have become. Consider the following:

- A bed-tracking system is only as good as the data used to populate it.

- Once the admitting department has found a bed for a new admission—even if the previous patient has not actually left—its job is done. The system is updated and a bed is assigned, but the patient is still sitting in the ED. Another way of accounting for the patient's true location must be found.

- Inpatient nursing, environmental services, and the bed coordinator all measure "task completion" differently. However, the hospital must ensure that someone is looking at the following two complex processes in their entirety:

  - Times from admission order to inpatient bed placement
  - Times from discharge order to having the bed empty, clean, and otherwise ready for the next patient (discharge turnaround time)

The process from admission order to inpatient bed placement includes at least the following checkpoints (some of which are not captured in traditional bed-management computer systems):

- Physician admit order
- Bed request
- Bed assignment
- Availability of bed assigned
- Report from ED nurse to inpatient nurse
- Patient transport
- Inpatient bed placement

The process from discharge order to bed availability includes at least the following checkpoints (some of which are not captured in traditional bed-management computer systems):

- Physician discharge order
- Nursing notification of discharge order
- Discharge assessment, teaching, and preparation
- Family notification
- Transportation

➔ Housekeeping triage systems

CONSIDER THIS WHEN:

Always

Successful environmental services departments have an effective system for triaging cleaning assignments that support efficient admission and transfer processes, and decrease the number of urgent or STAT requests for bed cleaning. These systems have the following features:

- Predefined targets for bed cleaning (from time of request to time of cleaning completion). These targets will vary by department or unit.

- A separate turnaround time is established for STAT cleaning requests. However, at some institutions, virtually all requests are STAT (which indicates that the initial turnaround targets were not appropriate or the environmental services department is consistently not meeting these targets). The percentage of STAT requests should be monitored for opportunities to improve service levels.

- Requests for cleaning are triaged by a designated individual—usually an environmental services supervisor—based on the above service guarantees. Note: A centralized triage approach for cleaning will probably not work well without a robust automated bed-tracking system.

- The "Bed Czar" (see below) has the ability to request changes in the order of cleaning.

➔ What is a Bed Czar?

CONSIDER THIS WHEN:

- There are significant delays in the admission process
- The ED is on paramedic diversion more than 40 hours per month
- Inpatients are routinely boarded in the ED
- The time it takes to admit an inpatient averages longer than one hour

As the name implies, a Bed Czar is someone with the power to initiate transportation for inpatient bed placement without asking permission. He or she is able to find open hospital beds and optimize functional capacity by ensuring smooth patient flows. He or she is held accountable for the effectiveness of the inpatient intake process. However, nursing management still controls the number of open beds.

An effective Bed Czar must have the following:

- A strong clinical background so that patient safety and appropriateness remain in the forefront (not to mention credibility with nursing managers and staff)

- Access to accurate and timely information, including the diversion status of the ED, the data necessary for efficient bed tracking, and the surgery schedule

- The undisputed authority of the nurse executive and the CEO in matters of bed placement

Consider more than one Bed Czar if there are more than 200 open beds.

➔ Bed briefings

CONSIDER THIS WHEN:
- There are significant delays in the admission process
- The ED is on paramedic diversion more than 40 hours per month
- Inpatients are routinely boarded in the ED
- The time it takes to admit an inpatient averages longer than one hour

Routine bed briefings have been established at many hospitals to enhance communication related to bed availability. They can be very successful at getting folks on the same page. Take care, however, to ensure that everyone at the table has the same goal: to enhance bed availability when there are peaks in demand.

← Assessment and discharge nurses

CONSIDER THIS WHEN:
- There are significant delays in the admission process
- The ED is on paramedic diversion more than 40 hours per month
- Inpatients are routinely boarded in the ED
- The time it takes to admit an inpatient averages longer than one hour

One common barrier to admitting a patient from the ED is the availability of an inpatient nurse to take the patient. There can be frequent delays in responses from the inpatient unit to take reports from the ED nurse on an admission, usually because the inpatient nurse is very busy and is reluctant or unable to take on the responsibility of a new patient.

When a new admission reaches the floor, the nurse may not have the time necessary to promptly complete an initial assessment, which will help set the stage for a successful hospitalization. Therefore, some hospitals are experimenting with admission and discharge nurses.

Nursing typically prioritizes duties as follows:

First, caring for the immediate and emerging needs of patients and requests from the patients' physicians (STAT medications and other needs).

Second, administering routine medications and performing routine, ongoing assessment.

Third, performing initial assessments.

Fourth, discharging a patient.

Fifth, taking on a new patient assignment.

As you review these priorities, you will note that the more critical steps to improving patient flow (appropriately) are not the most important aspects for the inpatient nurse.

Assigning a separate nurse to admit and discharge patients will move these throughput priorities to the top, and can make a big difference on the entire inpatient process. These nurses float to where admissions or discharges are required. You will run across the following issues when considering this approach:

- How these nurses affect overall nurse staffing will be tricky. It is unlikely that they will be entirely extra staff. They will often need to be worked into the existing nursing hours per patient day budget. Consider assigning nurses to this duty rather than sending them home due to drops in census.

- A nurse is not a nurse is not a nurse. Float nurses may not require the entire competency set of every unit they assist, but there may be limitations to the patient populations certain nurses are comfortable with. For example, not many nurses are equally comfortable with the needs of pediatric and adult patients.

- Having a separate nurse admit or transfer a patient puts another person in the communication loop, further complicating the process. To ensure safe and efficient care, these handoffs (from the admission nurse to the ongoing care nurse, and from the ongoing care nurse to the discharge nurse) should be carefully planned.

- It is essential to measure the effect of this approach. Study the process carefully during development to see what works and what doesn't. Are patients truly processed more quickly? What is the staffing cost or benefit of the model? What do nursing staff members think of the process? Implement this program only after you're confident that the process is well designed and accomplishes the desired result.

Express admission units

CONSIDER THIS WHEN:

- There are significant delays in the admission process
- The ED does not have the functional capacity to accommodate direct admissions

SEPARATE UNITS PROMOTE VARYING MINDSETS

Hospitals have found that clinical systems cannot always shift gears instantaneously. A unit geared toward very quick turnaround times does not do well with longer-term patients. Longer-term units are likewise unable to consistently accomplish patient turnaround quickly. We've classified units into three categories according to the pace of assessments and interventions—from fastest to deliberate. For a number of reasons, it is difficult for a fast-paced care unit to become deliberate, and it seems impossible for a deliberate unit to become fast paced. (Note: We observe that different speeds of care are safe and appropriate for the different portions of the patient's stay or clinical condition. It becomes a matter of matching the patient need to the correctly paced unit.)

- **Medical screening (pace = fastest)**: Average length of stay target is 2.5 hours. This is the ideal ED, geared toward diagnosis, immediate stabilization, and disposition.
- **Express admission units (pace = fast)**: Patient stays average less than four hours. The initial work-up has been done, but the patient still needs quick interventions while waiting for an inpatient bed. (Read more about this type of unit on p. 124.)
- **Observation units (pace = intermediate)**: Patient stays average less than 24 hours.
- **Inpatient units (pace = deliberate)**

The express admission unit is distinct from the ED and the observation unit. These units are established to provide a safe and appropriately focused location for newly admitted inpatients. Patients typically come from three sources, the ED, physician offices, or other institutions.

The unit is used to give the first doses of the inpatient medication regimen, start intravenous antibiotics, etc. It also becomes very useful in decompressing the ED.

WARNING:

An express admission unit may become a location in which you choose to house boarded patients for extensive periods of time. That is not the intent of the unit, but it may become necessary. However, if and when it becomes necessary to use the unit for this purpose, leadership should realize that the hospital no longer has an express admission unit.

➔ Flexible admission criteria

CONSIDER THIS WHEN:

Always

There has been tension between specialists and generalists throughout history. (If you have time for a fascinating read on this topic, we recommend *Guns, Germs and Steel* by Jarad Diamond, a seminal work on using the scientific method to study human history that explodes many myths about the why and how of contemporary human society. But, back to the crisis at hand!) Along with the growth of medical specialties has come the pressure to create nursing specialties. It does make sense, after all: with advances in pharmacological and other clinical technologies, staying current and maintaining competency is a struggle.

Nursing units have accordingly become more specialized. Although hospitals have become accustomed to intensive care, step down and medical/surgical units for adults, many hospitals now have a complex menu of specialty units: telemetry, surgical step down, neurology, orthopedics, post-cardiac care units, etc. Although the advantages are evident on the nursing and physician end, the Balkanization of the medical/surgical tower in a large hospital unnecessarily impedes the care process, and will keep patients waiting unnecessarily for the right kind of hospital bed to open up.

If this sounds familiar, we strongly recommend that you take a look at the admitting criteria for the various domains in your hospital. It is usually possible to expand the admitting criteria for the various units to include patients with similar—although not precisely identical—needs. It can make a big difference in patient flow.

SUBPROCESS 5

INPATIENT THROUGHPUT

Subprocess 5

INPATIENT THROUGHPUT

You're probably thinking, "As if this book weren't ambitious enough, imagine trying to tackle the entire inpatient stay. What nerve!"

Well, we will touch on this issue, but solving inpatient throughput difficulties is truly a journey rather than a destination. The inpatient stay is often affected most by macro approaches such as smoothing, clinical practice guidelines, rounding teams and other fundamental changes to the way physicians practice in the hospital.

We will nevertheless share a few "quick hits" that can affect patient stays.

→ Care paths and clinical pathways

CONSIDER THIS WHEN:

Always

JCAHO and others, such as the Institute for Healthcare Improvement, have been talking about the need for hospitals to develop clinical pathways for many years. JCAHO may be on the verge of requiring some, but don't hold your breath.

However, there are many—and there can by many more—"care paths" (sometimes called clinical protocols) that guide the hospitalization process. These are simply road maps—predetermined, integrated patient care plans—that describe what to expect during the hospitalization of a given patient population. Most common in surgical specialties, care paths usually describe what to expect from postoperative day one to discharge. To the extent that they are accurate, care paths are wonderful in helping patients recover quickly and leave for home on time. Some have also used them as powerful utilization management tools.

Care paths are very physician-driven, even though they mostly discuss nursing and ancillary services. Therefore, to develop accurate and useful care paths, you'll need data to support the pathway—how many stay on the pathway, how many fall off and why, outcomes, etc. It is also necessary to engage physician leaders and individual attending physicians in the development of pathways.

Many hospitals have developed a number of care paths only to have them collect dust on the shelf. Why? We believe it's because it takes a lot of focus and analysis to develop and maintain a truly accurate care path. It therefore becomes essential to focus care paths on the most common or complex cases. Once the first few become habit, move on to develop others.

Successful care paths are beginning to include the post-hospital care continuum (e.g., home care, ambulatory care, etc.). Consider extending care planning into the postdischarge phase—it can make a big difference in the discharge planning and patient education processes.

Make sure that all affected disciplines are involved in the development and monitoring of care paths.

Start with what has worked elsewhere: The National Electron Library for Health (part of the United Kingdom's National Health Service), for example, has a care path development database that is one particularly comprehensive resource (*www.nelh.nhs.uk/carepathways/*).

Be aware of the potential pitfalls of this approach:

- Care pathways take time to develop and significant focus and resources to successfully implement.
- Most care paths are experience-based rather than evidence-based.
- If physician practices vary greatly, developing a single care pathway will be difficult, time consuming, and prone to failure.
- Change of any kind is always difficult, and a care path usually means changing some staff practices.
- There have been instances in which care paths have been overused as a strict utilization tool. It is important to remember that a number of patients will appropriately fall off the path prior to discharge.

➔ Continuum of care strategies

CONSIDER THIS WHEN:

Always

Continuum of care strategies are sometimes framed as "care management programs." These strategies and programs are aimed at improving the outcomes and supporting the care of a specified group of hospitalized patients and patients who have chronic illnesses. For example, many organizations have successfully implemented care management programs for heart failure, end stage renal disease, and chronic obstructive pulmonary disease, to name a few.

These programs, which integrate aspects from the entire health continuum, can be very effective in planning and facilitating discharge. By involving all appropriate aspects of the continuum (e.g., the physician's office setting, home care agency, family, patient, nursing facility, etc.) the patient's care opportunities can be maximized and their clinical status closely monitored.

Successful continuum of care strategies focus on all aspects of care provided by the hospital (education, dietary services, outpatient rehabilitation, etc.), and involve ongoing communication and coordination regarding the patient's clinical status and care delivery options.

We have observed hospitals without such continuum of care strategies struggle with extended lengths of stay, higher costs, and billing difficulties due to lack of communication and coordination all along the continuum.

Here are some concrete tips to better manage the continuum of care:

- Related services, such as physical rehabilitation, short-term inpatient rehabilitation, or skilled nursing, should be managed along the same product line
- Case managers should have a clear understanding of appropriate referrals for the entire continuum of care needs
- A patient's clinical status should dictate his or her placement within the hospital, not just bed availability or cost
- Physicians and staff should be reminded of appropriate options for care other than the traditional inpatient setting

→ Scheduling discharges

CONSIDER THIS WHEN:

The average discharge takes more than two hours

In its Innovations Series for 2003, the Institute for Healthcare Improvement notes that some institutions have been successful in setting a discharge time with the patient on the day prior to discharge. It seems that 80% of the time, physicians and nurses can predict which patients will be discharged the next day. With this kind of advance notice, staff can begin to work on the multitude of discharge tasks well in advance.

→ Discharge planning/case management for inpatients

CONSIDER THIS WHEN:

Always

The purpose of case management (sometimes called utilization review/management, or the discharge planning department) is to assess and improve the care delivery process for all patients, regardless of payment source.

The case manager becomes involved with the patient at admission, screening his or her condition against established guidelines to confirm that hospital care is appropriate. The case manager remains involved through concurrent reviews to ensure that hospitalization continues to be indicated, and to work with the patient, physicians, and nursing staff to anticipate postdischarge needs and facilitate timely discharges by completing necessary tasks early in the care process.

SUBPROCESS 6

INPATIENT OUTPUT

Subprocess 6

INPATIENT OUTPUT

At last we've come to the final of our seven subprocesses: inpatient output, or discharge. Unlike inpatient throughput, the discharge process is finite with a number of proven, effective improvement strategies.

➔ Early physician discharge rounds

CONSIDER THIS WHEN:

- The hospital has a midnight census of 90% or more of the operational capacity more than half the time
- More than 2% of the hospital's patients are boarded in the ED or PACU on most days

As demonstrated earlier, the demand for inpatient beds grows as the day goes on. Therefore, it would be best if patients could be discharged in the morning rather than the afternoon. Yet it remains common for physicians to discharge patients in the afternoon rather than the morning. It's easy to understand why:

- Physicians are more focused on performing surgery at the beginning of the day, saving the afternoons for rounding on that day's patients and patients who could potentially be discharged.
- Teaching institutions have educational rounds in the morning that last three hours or so. Patients who are ready for discharge are not typically part of those rounds.
- Discharge often depends on a laboratory value or other test results from the day of discharge. Although it is theoretically possible for the physician to write an order such as "discharge if a.m. potassium is within normal limits," there have been a number of misadventures involved with the practice, and physicians and hospitals are reluctant to tempt fate.
- If there are two patients to be assessed—one a new admission and one a potential discharge—the clinician will usually take care of the new admission first. The new admission normally needs more clinical attention than does the patient who appears ready to go home.

So what's a physician to do?

First, don't give up, but also recognize the obstacles. Second, develop other strategies to help the physician discharge the patient earlier rather than later. Consider the following approaches:

- Allocate surgery block times for same-day admissions (surgery patients who will be admitted rather than discharged after the procedure) based on the total number of elective inpatients in the house. That way the surgeon will be motivated to discharge one of his or her inpatients before operating on another patient who will need admission after surgery. This heavy-handed approach may be the last resort.
- Establish systems between the nursing and laboratory departments to ensure that testing results are on the medical record by 6 a.m.
- Develop care paths that call for patient readiness of discharge on the morning of the last day.
- Use physician assistants and nurse practitioners to assist the physician in the last day, pre-discharge evaluation.
- Consider developing hospital rounding teams. This strategy is most plausible in an integrated health care delivery system, such as a university, specialty hospital, or health care network.

→ Timeliness of transportation

CONSIDER THIS WHEN:

It takes longer than two hours after a physician's order to discharge the average (median) patient

There appear to be many slips between the call for transportation and the actual transportation of the patient. Although this may not be an issue at your institution, many have found it necessary to measure and improve the transportation process. There are several reasons why this may make sense:

- The transportation process is easily measured and tracked if there is a good electronic transportation management system, thereby making accountability and monitoring improvements simple. These systems are even more effective if they are integrated with an electronic bed-management system.
- Improving transportation processes is conducive to the Lean improvement approach, which uses very clever techniques for uncovering wasted steps in a process.
- Transportation staffing can be adjusted based on the number of transport requests by hour of day and the normal amount of time it takes to complete a transport.

Visual cueing systems for discharge

CONSIDER THIS WHEN:

It takes more than two hours to discharge the average (median) patient

There are many steps in the discharge process, but they all begin with a physician's order. However, the chart may not be immediately available once the physician decides on discharge; the physician still needs to write a note summarizing the care, and may even dictate a discharge summary before giving the chart back to the ward clerk for processing.

Why not get a head start on the discharge process? Some hospitals have implemented a visual cue that, believe it or not, can cut significant time off the discharge process: a flag on the door of the patient's room. As the physician exits the room, he or she raises the flag as a cue to the ward clerk that a discharge order is on the way. The discharge process can then begin.

Other visual cues include a discharge chart rack, where the physician places the chart to let all involved know that the patient is ready to be sent home.

Inpatient chart rack systems

CONSIDER THIS WHEN:

It takes more than two hours to discharge the average (median) patient

Some hospitals have gone way beyond the visual flag for discharged patients described above. They have implemented a formal chart rack system just like the ED, so that all involved know when there are new orders on the chart, when results have been returned that the physician needs to see, etc. It will be interesting to learn exactly how far such systems can go to expedite care.

Lining up the discharge process

CONSIDER THIS WHEN:

Always

The discharge process has many steps, including writing a nursing discharge assessment, obtaining discharge supplies and medications, gathering patient educational materials, etc.

We feel it is essential to treat inpatient discharge just like any other complex process: by scripting and anticipating the steps that are to come. A discharge checklist, just like the preflight checklist in the cockpit of a 747, should come in handy. As each step is checked off/initialed, the charge nurse or ward clerk can anticipate the next steps, which are more likely to be completed quickly if there is a mutually envisioned process.

It is easy to work discharge tasks throughout the last day of admission, but it is very difficult to fit everything in if the team waits until the last minute.

APPENDICES

Appendix A

IMPROVEMENT STRATEGIES

Massaging the data: Cool analysis techniques

The ways in which data can be converted to information are endless. We've decided to share a few of our favorites.

HIRING A DATA ANALYST

Clinical leaders should have the ability to interpret data about their departments and clinical systems, but they should not be expected to develop the data displays themselves. How can a talented clinical leader carefully select an analyst to hire? One of the most talented clinical leaders we know is admittedly computer illiterate—spreadsheets make her hands sweat and her hair hurt. She knows enough to recruit some very top-notch analysts who make her data sing. Here are some tips so you can do the same thing:

- Have the candidates bring their favorite Microsoft Excel data displays, and have him or her explain how you should interpret them. If it's a pie chart, say, "Next candidate please."

- Show the candidates the data displays in this book. When they say they would have no trouble recreating them in Microsoft Excel (which they all will), show them to a computer and give them an hour or two to generate one of the charts.

- Ask whether they've ever studied statistical process control. If so, ask them to explain to you in general terms what an upper control limit is, what it means when a single point is beyond the limit, and what it means when a series of data points within the upper and lower limits is significant.

- Ask them whether they know what a pivot table is. If they know, have them make one for you.

Good luck. With the right analyst, you and your institution will go far.

IMPROVEMENT APPROACHES

In the chapter "Subprocess zero" we discussed the keys to improvement. Here we list a few approaches that have proven useful throughout the industry.

Measures: The first step in improvement

Regardless of the selected approach, apply it to the data you will collect.

Virtually all "broken" health care systems are nonfunctional because leaders do not have ready access to meaningful data that measure these broken systems and processes. Therefore, whatever improvement techniques you use, start by improving the data collection. Do not start trying to improve the process until you do some sort of Plan-Do-Check-Act cycle on the data.

Lean

Toyota comes through again. By inventing Lean improvement techniques, the car company was able to show the way to simplifying and improving complex processes. A number of consulting groups and institutions put these techniques to very good use in solving health care problems.

Six Sigma

Six Sigma, also adopted from other industries, is very "in" right now, and for good reason. Six Sigma has a wealth of powerful improvement models and data analysis techniques. Companies pay thousands of dollars to get their improvement gurus to become "Six Sigma black belts."

We like the Six Sigma techniques very much. Their main focus is on minimizing defects rather than on eliminating steps in a process. Some experts have gleaned very powerful results from combining Lean with Six Sigma.

iDelta

We like our own system, iDelta, best of all. Why? Because it's ours. Also, because we think it is very practical for health care. iDelta incorporates the best of Demming, Juran, Lean, and Six Sigma with our own flavor of "rapid-cycle testing."

What distinguishes iDelta from other approaches? It's fast, it works, and it lasts. However, we must confess a fair share of bias in our recommendation.

Appendix B

EXCERPTED FROM "GUIDELINE FOR HAND HYGIENE IN HEALTH-CARE SETTING: RECOMMENDATION OF THE HEALTHCARE INFECTION CONTROL PRACTICES ADVISORY COMMITTEE AND THE HICPAC/SHEA/APIC/IDSA HAND HYGIENE TASK FORCE, MMWR, OCTOBER 23, 2002/52 (RR16); 1-44"

Full text and related information is available at www.cdc.gov/handhygiene/.

Recommendations:

1. Indications for handwashing and hand antisepsis

A. When hands are visibly dirty or contaminated with proteinaceous material or are visibly soiled with blood or other body fluids, wash hands with either a non-antimicrobial soap and water or an antimicrobial soap and water.

B. If hands are not visibly soiled, use an alcohol-based hand rub for routinely decontaminating hands . . . Alternatively, wash hands with an antimicrobial soap and water.

C. Decontaminate hands before having direct contact with patients.

D. Decontaminate hands before donning sterile gloves when inserting a central intravascular catheter.

E. Decontaminate hands before inserting indwelling urinary catheters, peripheral vascular catheters, or other invasive devices that do not require a surgical procedure.

F. Decontaminate hands after contact with a patient's intact skin (e.g., when taking a pulse or blood pressure, and lifting a patient).

G. Decontaminate hands after contact with body fluids or excretions, mucous membranes, nonintact skin, and wound dressings if hands are not visibly soiled.

H. Decontaminate hands if moving from a contaminated-body site to a clean-body site during patient care.

I. Decontaminate hands after contact with inanimate objects (including medical equipment) in the immediate vicinity of the patient.

J. Decontaminate hands after removing gloves.

K. Before eating and after using a restroom, wash hands with a non-antimicrobial soap and water or with an antimicrobial soap and water.

L. Antimicrobial-impregnated wipes (i.e., towelettes) may be considered as an alternative to washing hands with non-antimicrobial soap and water. Because they are not as effective as alcohol-based hand rubs or washing hands with an antimicrobial soap and water for reducing bacterial counts on the hands of HCWs, they are not a substitute for using an alcohol-based hand rub or antimicrobial soap.

M. *Wash hands with non-antimicrobial soap and water or with antimicrobial soap and water if exposure to Bacillus anthracis is suspected or proven. The physical action of washing and rinsing hands under such circumstances is recommended because alcohols, chlorhexidine, iodophors, and other antiseptic agents have poor activity against spores.*

N. No recommendation can be made regarding the routine use of nonalcohol-based hand rubs for hand hygiene in health-care settings. Unresolved issue.

2. Hand-hygiene technique

A. When decontaminating hands with an alcohol-based hand rub, apply product to palm of one hand and rub hands together, covering all surfaces of hands and fingers, until hands are dry . . . Follow the manufacturer's recommendations regarding the volume of product to use.

B. When washing hands with soap and water, wet hands first with water, apply an amount of product recommended by the manufacturer to hands, and rub hands together vigorously for at least 15 seconds, covering all surfaces of the hands and fingers. Rinse hands with water and dry thoroughly with a disposable towel. Use towel to turn off the faucet . . . Avoid using hot water, because repeated exposure to hot water may increase the risk of dermatitis.

C. Liquid, bar, leaflet or powdered forms of plain soap are acceptable when washing hands with a non-antimicrobial soap and water. When bar soap is used, soap racks that facilitate drainage and small bars of soap should be used.

D. Multiple-use cloth towels of the hanging or roll type are not recommended for use in health-care settings.

3. Surgical hand antisepsis

A. Remove rings, watches, and bracelets before beginning the surgical hand scrub.

B. Remove debris from underneath fingernails using a nail cleaner under running water.

C. Surgical hand antisepsis using either an antimicrobial soap or an alcohol-based hand rub with persistent activity is recommended before donning sterile gloves when performing [some] surgical procedures.

D. When performing surgical hand antisepsis using an antimicrobial soap, scrub hands and forearms for the length of time recommended by the manufacturer, usually 2–6 minutes. Long scrub times (e.g., 10 minutes) are not necessary.

E. When using an alcohol-based surgical hand-scrub product with persistent activity, follow the manufacturer's instructions. Before applying the alcohol solution, prewash hands and forearms with a non-antimicrobial soap and dry hands and forearms completely. After application of the alcohol-based product as recommended, allow hands and forearms to dry thoroughly before donning sterile gloves.

4. Selection of hand-hygiene agents

A. Provide personnel with efficacious hand-hygiene products that have low irritancy potential, particularly when these products are used multiple times per shift . . . This recommendation applies to products used for hand antisepsis before and after patient care in clinical areas and to products used for surgical hand antisepsis by surgical personnel.

B. To maximize acceptance of hand-hygiene products by HCWs, solicit input from these employees regarding the feel, fragrance, and skin tolerance of any products under consideration. The cost of hand-hygiene products should not be the primary factor influencing product selection.

C. When selecting non-antimicrobial soaps, antimicrobial soaps, or alcohol-based hand rubs, solicit information from manufacturers regarding any known interactions between products used to clean hands, skin care products, and the types of gloves used in the institution.

D. Before making purchasing decisions, evaluate the dispenser systems of various product manufacturers or distributors to ensure that dispensers function adequately and deliver an appropriate volume of product.

E. Do not add soap to a partially empty soap dispenser. This practice of "topping off" dispensers can lead to bacterial contamination of soap.

5. Skin care

A. Provide HCWs with hand lotions or creams to minimize the occurrence of irritant contact dermatitis associated with hand antisepsis or handwashing.

B. Solicit information from manufacturers regarding any effects that hand lotions, creams, or alcohol-based hand antiseptics may have on the persistent effects of antimicrobial soaps being used in the institution.

6. Other Aspects of Hand Hygiene

A. Do not wear artificial fingernails or extenders when having direct contact with patients at high risk (e.g., those in intensive-care units or operating rooms).

B. Keep natural nails tips less than 1/4-inch long.

C. Wear gloves when contact with blood or other potentially infectious materials, mucous membranes, and nonintact skin could occur.

D. Remove gloves after caring for a patient. Do not wear the same pair of gloves for the care of more than one patient, and do not wash gloves between uses with different patients.

E. Change gloves during patient care if moving from a contaminated body site to a clean body site.

F. No recommendation can be made regarding wearing rings in health-care settings. Unresolved issue.

7. Health-care worker educational and motivational programs

A. As part of an overall program to improve hand-hygiene practices of HCWs, educate personnel regarding the types of patient-care activities that can result in hand contamination and the advantages and disadvantages of various methods used to clean their hands.

B. Monitor HCWs' adherence with recommended hand-hygiene practices and provide personnel with information regarding their performance.

C. Encourage patients and their families to remind HCWs to decontaminate their hands.

8. Administrative measures

A. Make improved hand-hygiene adherence an institutional priority and provide appropriate administrative support and financial resources.

B. Implement a multidisciplinary program designed to improve adherence of health personnel to recommended hand-hygiene practices.

C. As part of a multidisciplinary program to improve hand-hygiene adherence, provide HCWs with a readily accessible alcohol-based hand-rub product.

D. To improve hand-hygiene adherence among personnel who work in areas in which high workloads and high intensity of patient care are anticipated, make an alcohol-based hand rub available at the entrance to the patient's room or at the bedside, in other convenient locations, and in individual pocket-sized containers to be carried by HCWs.

E. Store supplies of alcohol-based hand rubs in cabinets or areas approved for flammable materials.

Performance indicators:

1. The following performance indicators are recommended for measuring improvements in HCWs' hand-hygiene adherence:

A. Periodically monitor and record adherence as the number of hand-hygiene episodes performed by personnel/number of hand-hygiene opportunities, by ward or by service. Provide feedback to personnel regarding their performance.

B. Monitor the volume of alcohol-based hand rub (or detergent used for handwashing or hand antisepsis) used per 1,000 patient-days.

C. Monitor adherence to policies dealing with wearing of artificial nails.

D. When outbreaks of infection occur, assess the adequacy of health-care worker hand hygiene.

Name:

Medical Record No.

Date of Birth

IMPRINT of PATIENT ID

SAMPLE INTERHOSPITAL TRANSFER SUMMARY

SECTION I – Patient Information

ADDRESS		CITY	STATE	ZIP CODE	
AGE	SEX: ☐ Male ☐ Female	DIAGNOSIS			
DATE / TIME FIRST PRESENTED		REASONS FOR TRANSFER			

SECTION II – Patient Transfer Acknowledgement

I understand that I have the right to receive medical screening, examination, and evaluation by a physician, or other appropriate personnel, without regard to my ability to pay, prior to any transfer from this hospital and that I have a right to be informed of the reasons for any transfer. I acknowledge that I have received medical screening, examination, and evaluation by a physician, or other appropriate personnel and that I have been informed of the reasons and agree to my transfer.

Signature:_____ Relationship:_____ Date:_____ Time:_____ AM / PM
(Patient or representative)

SECTION III – Physician Certification – (Completed by Transferring Physician)

I, *(name of physician, please print)*_____, the undersigned physician, have examined and

Evaluated *(name of patient)*_____.

Please check one of the following:
- ☐ Stable for Transfer: I am assured within reasonable clinical confidence that no material deterioration in the patient's medical condition will occur as a result of the transfer. I believe that the receiving facility has the capability to manage the patient's medical condition and any reasonable foreseeable complication of that condition.
- ☐ Unstable for Transfer and Women in Labor: Based upon the information available at the time of transfer, the medical benefits reasonably expected from the provision of appropriate medical treatment at another medical facility outweigh the increased risks to the individual or, in the case of a woman in labor, to the woman or the unborn child, from being transferred.

Summary of Benefits: ☐ Continuity of Care ☐ Specialized facilities/services/personnel ☐ Clinical services ☐ Other:	Summary of Risks: ☐ Negligible ☐ Time delay in receiving treatment ☐ Deterioration of medical condition ☐ Other:	**Transferring Physician Signature:** _____

SECTION IV – Accepting Facility and Physician Transfer Information

The receiving facility *(name)*, _____, has the capability and capacity to manage the patient's condition and any reasonably foreseeable complication of that condition and accepts the patient as acknowledged by:

Name/Title of **Supervisor, Bed Control or Admitting** at Receiving Facility:	Location	PHONE #	Spoken To By Whom: (Name/Title)	Military Time
Name of **Accepting MD or Designee** at Receiving Facility:	Location	PHONE #	Spoken To By Whom: (Name/Title)	Military Time

SECTION V – Transfer Assessment

MEDICAL RECORDS AND TEST RESULTS WERE PROVIDED:	☐ Transfer forms ☐ ED / L&D Records ☐ Nurses Notes ☐ Patient Belongings	☐ Lab ☐ Radiology ☐ EKG ☐ Other (Please Indicate)	MODE OF TRANSPORTATION: ☐ CCT/MD ☐ CCT/RN ☐ ACLS / Paramedic ☐ BLS ☐ OTHER

PHYSICIAN ASSESSMENT: Transfer nursing assessment reviewed. Patient's condition remains compatible with transfer. **MD Signature:** _____ Printed Name: _____		Military Time
RN Assessment: (See nurses notes for nursing assessment and transfer summary) This transfer form and documentation packet is complete according to hospital policy and procedure. **RN Signature:** _____ Printed Name: _____	DATE	Military Time

Should you have any complaints concerning the services you have received from this hospital, you may contact:
Name of State Agency
Distribution: ORIGINAL = chart * CANARY = Receiving Hospital * PINK = Department * GOLD = Patient * Copy original for Ambulance

USE AND PLACEMENT OF "WHITE BOARDS"

Balancing Safe and Efficient Operations with Patient Confidentiality and Privacy

White boards

A white board or a patient assignment/location board is a common fixture in health care settings. In recent years they have drawn the attention of JCAHO and DHS reviewers on routine surveys and complaint visits. Other questions have arisen with the advent of HIPAA. There are no strict rules for where white boards may/should be placed or what information may be put on the board. Therefore, each medical center is challenged to strike a balance between operations and confidentiality that both protects privacy and promotes safety and efficiency. White boards fall under the general rule for compliance with non-specific standards: **"Say What You Do and Do What You Say."**

Is A White board Necessary?

Carefully evaluate whether patient care can be SAFELY given without a white board. If it can, then the white board should not be installed or used.

Once management determines that patient safety and efficiency is at issue rather than staff preference or institutional inertia, a few words should be written in a policy that explains/justifies the use of a white board and sets limits on the information it should contain.

Placement

White boards should, to the extent possible, be placed where only authorized staff can view them. However, regardless of the nature of the personnel viewing the board, information should be limited to only absolutely essential information.

Patient Name

Recommendations:
- Use last name and first initial.
- Have a flag (e.g., "«") for "name alerts" (e.g., when there are two people on the unit with similar names ... Bud Smith and Brad Smith, or Celia Franklin and Cecile Franklin).

• Have a well-implemented John Doe policy:

Inform patients that, for their safety, their names will be placed on a white board where other caregivers can see it. As appropriate, let them know that their last names and first initials may also be visible to the others walking down the hallway. Give the patients the option of going under assumed names. This information can be included in one of the many patient safety pamphlets currently under development.

Other Information

Indicating staff assignments on a white board is rarely a problem. However, clinical information should be coded and used only when absolutely necessary. For example:

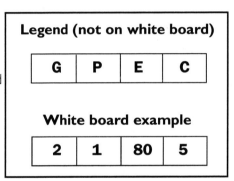

Legend (not on white board)			
G	P	E	C

White board example			
2	1	80	5

• A red square magnet (■) can be placed next to the name of an emergency department patient who has a radiology procedure pending. A blue triangle (▲) can be used for other studies, etc.
• In labor and delivery, a standard grid without labels could be used for the usual labor monitoring signs. In the example at right, the unlabeled boxes stand for Gravida, Para, Effacement, and Minutes Between Contractions. Nurses and providers (MDs, CNMs) would be acquainted with this simple code upon unit orientation.
• Perioperative can put any staffing information they wish (surgeon, assistant, scrub, etc.) However, the type of procedure to be performed should be as abstract as possible.

What NOT to Put On the White board

Regardless of the placement of the white board, it should never contain certain information. For example, the board should not contain

❑ Clinical diagnosis
❑ Results of diagnostic testing
❑ Any clinical information (Exception: codes that communicate clinical information ONLY to appropriate staff. These codes should only be used when absolutely necessary.)

NOTES

NOTES

NOTES

NOTES

_____

_____

_____

_____

_____

_____

_____

_____

_____

_____

_____

_____